The
TREASURE BAG

STORIES AND POEMS SELECTED BY

Lena Barksdale

Illustrated by Maurice Brevannes

Alfred · A · Knopf : New York

THIS IS A BORZOI BOOK,
PUBLISHED BY ALFRED A. KNOPF, INC.

Contents

The Three Billy Goats Gruff 7

My Dog Chum 10

The Rock-a-By Lady by Eugene Field 14

The Fox and the Grapes 16

The Months by Sara Coleridge 17

The Teacup Whale by Lydia Gibson 18

For Good Luck 32

Ten Little Squirrels 33

The Pirate and the Pickled Onions by Rose Fyleman 34

Thirty White Horses—A Riddle 37

The Three Bears 38

The Ice-Cream Man by Rachel Field 44

A Strange Little Home by Alice Gall and Fleming Crew 46

My Steam Shovel by Vera Edelstadt 52

Cinderella 54

The Swing by Robert Louis Stevenson 68

Mr. Easter Rabbit by Carolyn Sherwin Bailey 69

Nancy Etticoat—A Riddle 74

The Lamb by William Blake 75

Names by Dorothy Aldis 76

The Little Boy Who Wouldn't Get Up by Rose Fyleman 77

Specky and Her Family 80

Valentine to My Mother by Christina Rosetti 85

Puss in Boots 86

The Dog and His Shadow 94

Counting-Out Rhyme 95

How the Little Owl's Name Was Changed by Charles E. Gillham . . 96

Dominick-Tekun: A Basque Legend by Frances Carpenter 102

The Fox and the Crane 110

Robin and Pussy 111

The Silly Old Woman 112

The Special Fourth of July by Lavinia R. Davis 113

The Hare and the Tortoise 122

The Frog Who Wanted to Be as Big as the Ox 124

Little Orphant Annie by James Whitcomb Riley 126

DOLL IN THE GRASS: *A Norwegian Folk Tale*
by Ingri and Edgar Parin d' Aulaire 128
NURSERY RHYMES FROM CHINA Translated by Isaac Taylor Headland . . 132
MISS T. by Walter de la Mare 134
NONSENSE VERSES by Laura E. Richards 135
THE SHIRE COLT by Zhenya and Jan Gay 136
THANKSGIVING DAY by L. Maria Child 148
THE HOUSE THAT JACK BUILT 150
THE TRAIN THAT WOULD NOT STAY ON THE TRACK
by Caroline D. Emerson 153
PIPPA'S SONG by Robert Browning 157
TABLE MANNERS by Gelett Burgess 158
LIMERICK by Edward Lear 158
THANK YOU, GOD, by Ilo Orleans 159

The stories for which no author is credited have been retold by Lena Barksdale.

The Three Billy Goats Gruff

Once on a time there were three Billy Goats, who were to go up to the hillside to make themselves fat, and the family name of the goats was "Gruff."

On the way up was a bridge, over a river, which they had to cross, and under the bridge lived an ugly Troll with eyes as big as saucers, and a nose as long as a poker.

First of all came the youngest Billy Goat Gruff to cross the bridge. "Trip, trap; trip, trap!" went the bridge.

"Who's that tripping over my bridge?" roared the Troll.

"Oh, it is only I, the tiniest Billy Goat Gruff, and I'm going

7

up to the hillside to make myself fat," said the Billy Goat with such a small voice.

"Now, I'm coming to gobble you up," said the Troll.

"Oh, no! Pray do not take me: I'm too little, that I am," said the Billy Goat. "Wait a bit till the second Billy Goat Gruff comes —he's much bigger."

"Well! Be off with you," said the Troll.

A little while after came the second Billy Goat Gruff across the bridge.

"Trip, trap! trip, trap! trip, trap!" went the bridge.

"Who is that tripping over my bridge?" roared the Troll.

"Oh, it's the second Billy Goat Gruff, and I'm going up to the hillside to make myself fat," said the Billy Goat. Nor had he such a small voice, either.

"Now, I'm coming to gobble you up!" said the Troll.

"Oh, no! Don't take me. Wait a little till the big Billy Goat comes; he's much bigger."

"Very well! Be off with you," said the Troll.

But just then came up the big Billy Goat Gruff.

"Trip, trap! trip, trap! trip, trap!" went the bridge.

"Who's that tramping on my bridge?" roared the Troll.

"It's I, the big Billy Goat Gruff," said the Billy Goat and he had a big hoarse voice.

"Now, I'm coming to gobble you up!" roared the Troll.

"Well come! I have two spears so stout,
With them I'll thrust your eyeballs out:
I have besides two great big stones,
With them I'll crush you, body and bones!"

That was what the big Billy Goat said; so he flew at the Troll, and thrust him with his horns, and crushed him to bits, body and bones, and tossed him out into the river, and after that he went up to the hillside.

There the Billy Goats got so fat that they were scarcely able to walk home again, and if they haven't grown thinner, why, they're still fat; and so—

"Snip, snap, stout.
This tale's told out."

My Dog Chum

Jimmy wrote this story. Jimmy was a little boy a very, very long time ago, about the time your grandpa was a little boy. Maybe your grandpa knew Jimmy. You might ask him. People didn't have trucks in those days; they drove horses hitched to wagons instead. But boys liked to coast, and they loved their dogs, just the same as they do today. Now Jimmy says:

The story I am going to tell you is a true story about my dog and me. I am six years old, but I think my dog must be about fifty, because I have had him ever since I could remember. His name is Chum, and he knows it, too, just as well as you know yours, and he's the smartest dog in the world. When I ask him if he wants his dinner, his tail wags yes. He can do most anything, so I am sure he could

wag no just as well, if he wanted to, but of course he wouldn't want to wag no to that sort of question.

The most funniest thing we do is to take turns being horse. My big brother made me a nice harness—not for me of course, but for Chum. I think Chum likes it as well as I do, because when I put it on him and fasten him to the sled and get on the sled and say, "Now, go it, Chummie!"—how he does go. He runs so fast nobody can catch him!

And, Oh boy! Does the wind whistle by my ears and the snow fly in my face! And all the people shout and wave when they see us whiz down the street, past the slow old horses just as easy!

Sometimes the farmers going into town on their wagons will race with us, and sometimes they have four horses hitched to their wagon. But when Chummie hears me call: "Hi, there! Stur, boy!" he just runs away from those slow old horses as if they were standing still.

Then the men who are cleaning off the sidewalks with snow shovels, and the boys who are delivering groceries—and most everybody—will stop to watch, and some of them will call, "Hurrah for Chummie!" or "Go it, Chummy boy, show 'em what you can do!" And the butcher, who is a good friend of mine, comes all the way out of his shop to give Chummie a piece of meat. Everybody pats Chummie on the head, and tells him he's a good fellow, and sometimes somebody gives me a lollypop because I own such a fine dog.

Then I put Chummie's harness on, and he gets on the sled, and I stick the whip in his collar. I carry the whip because the men do, but of course I never whip Chum. It would make him sorry, and he couldn't go any faster anyway.

Chum is a big heavy dog, and so I can't go very fast when I am pulling him, and then all the teams pass me on the road. I just call out to the men I have raced with, "Just you wait till Chum is the horse again, and we'll leave you way behind!" They laugh, and it makes me proud to hear them say:

"What a wonderful dog to sit so still and hold the reins in his mouth just as well as Jimmy holds them in his hands!"

I know a big boy, named Harvey, and he has a dog, named Gyp. Harvey coasts down the long hill by Mr. Judson's place, and when he gets to the bottom he ties a stout string to his sled, and Gyp takes the string in his mouth and pulls the sled uphill, all the way, so Harvey can coast down again. Sometimes Harvey falls in a snow drift, and Gyp digs to help him get out. Gyp makes that old snow fly, I can tell you! Then when it gets dark, and they have to go home to supper, Gyp walks along by Harvey's side, with his black tail curled over his back, and he never looks one bit tired!

Last summer when I was only five Mother let me go to pick berries, just with Chum. Chum was chasing rabbits most of the time, but if anything had scared me Chum would have been right there to take care of me. He would never let anything hurt me. Mother knew that. Next summer I am going to learn to swim. Chum loves to jump in the river and swim around, and he'll help me to learn. Then what fun we'll have!

I'm a lucky boy to have a fine dog like Chum!

The Rock-A-By Lady

By Eugene Field

The Rock-a-By Lady from Hushaby Street
    Comes stealing; comes creeping;
The poppies they hang from her head to her feet,
And each hath a dream that is tiny and fleet—
She bringeth her poppies to you, my sweet,
    When she findeth you sleeping!
There is one little dream of a beautiful drum—
    "Rub-a-dub!" it goeth;
There is one little dream of a big sugar-plum,
And lo! thick and fast the other dreams come
Of popguns that bang, and tin tops that hum,
    And a trumpet that bloweth!
And dollies peep out of those wee little dreams
    With laughter and singing;
And boats go a-floating on silvery streams,
And the stars peek-a-boo with their own misty gleams,
And up, and up, and up, where the Mother Moon beams,
    The fairies go winging!
Would you dream all these dreams that are tiny and fleet?
    They'll come to you sleeping;
So shut the two eyes that are weary, my sweet,
For the Rock-a-By Lady from Hushaby Street,
With poppies that hang from her head to her feet,
    Comes stealing; comes creeping.

The Fox and the Grapes

A Fox, passing a grape arbor, saw a luscious bunch of grapes hanging high above his head. "My, don't those grapes look good!" said the Fox to himself. Indeed they did look good; every grape on the bunch was round and ripe and perfect.

The Fox jumped up to get them, but the grapes were hanging some distance from the ground, and he missed them. He went a little way off, got a running start, and jumped again. Again he missed them. He jumped time and again, but he could not jump quite high enough to get the grapes.

At last he trotted off, saying, "I don't want those old grapes anyway. They can stay there until they rot for all I care. They are sour old things."

Now when you hear someone say, "Sour grapes!" think of this story, and you will know exactly what he means.

The Months

By Sara Coleridge

January brings the snow,
Makes our feet and fingers glow.
February brings the rain,
Thaws the frozen lake again,
March brings breezes sharp and chill,
Shakes the dancing daffodil.
April brings the primrose sweet,
Scatters daisies at our feet.
May brings flocks of pretty lambs,
Sporting round their fleecy dams.
June brings tulips, lilies, roses,
Fills the children's hands with posies.
Hot July brings thunder-showers,
Apricots, and gilly-flowers.
August brings the sheaves of corn;
Then the harvest home is borne.
Warm September brings the fruit;
Sportsmen then begin to shoot.
Brown October brings the pheasant;
Then to gather nuts is pleasant.
Dull November brings the blast—
Hark! the leaves are whirling fast.
Cold December brings the sleet,
Blazing fire, and Christmas treat.

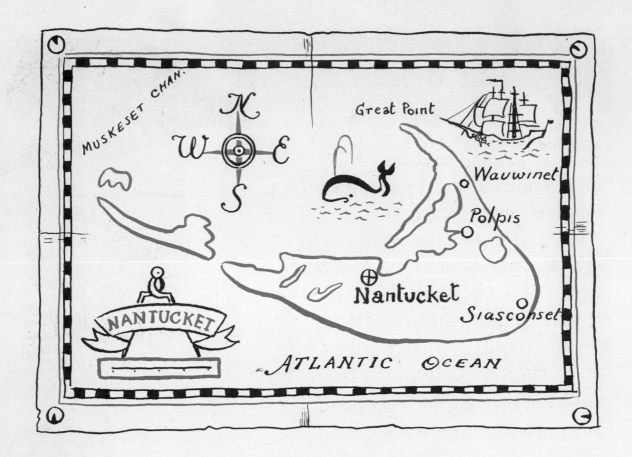

The Teacup Whale

By Lydia Gibson

One day early in spring David was going along the road, splish, splash, squish, squash. In spring when the snow has melted the road is very muddy. David came to a big puddle in the middle of the road. He had to walk around it because it was too big to jump over. Walking around took longer than jumping, so David got interested in the puddle on the way round, and he stopped to look in.

He saw pebbles and he saw bubbles and he saw mud. He saw some sticks floating, and he saw an early angleworm coming out for a springtime walk around the edge of the puddle. He saw a tiny

river running in one end of the puddle and another tiny river running out the other end, made of wheeltracks in the muddy road.

Then all of a sudden he saw a little black something in the middle of the puddle. It wiggled. It blew a tiny fountain. Then it went down out of sight under the muddy water. David crouched down to see better, and leaned over so far he almost fell in. For a minute all he could see in the puddle was himself, as if he were looking in a mirror, and the white clouds overhead in the blue sky. Then the tiny black thing came up to the top of the water and flopped its tiny black tail—kersplash!

"Why, my goodness gracious me!" said David, with his eyes bulging out. "It's a whale!"

He had a map of Nantucket on the wall beside his bed at home, with a picture of a whale on it. He knew exactly what a whale was like, from the spout that came out of his blowhole to the flukes of his spreading tail fully an inch away.

David luckily had his little tin bucket with him. He hardly ever went out without his little red tin bucket, it was so very useful for carrying all sorts of things home. This time he worked hard and splashed and puffed and caught the whale in his hands, and put it in the bucket with enough water to swim in, and he carried it home.

The bucket was quite deep and dark for such a tiny whale, and you couldn't see him very well, so David went and climbed on a chair, and reached on the shelf, and got a white teacup and filled it with water before he put in the whale. The whale showed up very black and shiny and handsome in the nice white teacup. Then he carried it to his mother.

"Whatever have you got there?" asked David's mother. "Another polliwog?"

"No," said David, "that's a whale."

"Nonsense," said his mother. "Whales are enormous."

"What is a nor-mouse?" asked David.

"Whales are," said his mother; it didn't make sense, but then very few things did. She went on: "It means very big indeed. Bigger than a horse. Bigger than a car. Bigger than an elephant. Whales are enormous. But what a very funny polliwog this is!"

Every day the whale grew. David fed him bits of chopped meat, and he got bigger and bigger, and he got stronger and stronger. One morning when David came down to breakfast the teacup was smashed into bits, and the whale lay flopping in the saucer in a few drops of water. He had grown too big and too strong for the little white teacup. So David went to the kitchen and got a strong yellow bowl, the kind they mix ginger cookies in. The whale swam in that, and it fitted him nicely. He went round and round and round to the left side and admired the scenery, and then he turned and went round and round and round to the right side and admired the scenery. He never seemed to get tired of doing it. For a good many days the whale swam in the yellow mixing bowl. But he was growing all the time. He ate boiled rice—at first ten grains a day, and then more and more. He got bigger and bigger and he got stronger and stronger. One day he gave a jump and landed on the floor. He was too big for the yellow bowl.

David sat down and put his elbows on his knees and put his chin in his hands. That was to make thinking easier. Then he thought what to do. The watering can was too small. The soup

22

kettle was too small. The brass fruit bowl was too small. The wash basin was too small, and, besides, they couldn't wash their hands if there was a whale in it. So he asked his mother if he could borrow the wash boiler. She said yes, if he would be careful of it. So the whale lived in the wash boiler. All the time he was getting bigger and bigger, and stronger and stronger, and the little fountains he blew through the blowpipe in the top of his head were getting bigger too, and he couldn't turn around.

"I do declare," said David's mother, "I never in all my born days saw a polliwog blow fountains through the top of his head! What a very funny polliwog!"

The whale lived in the wash boiler about a week. He knocked over the wash boiler one day, and made a big puddle on the floor, so David had to move him again. He thought and he thought. There wasn't any place in the house now big enough for the whale to turn round in but the bathtub. So David moved the whale into the bathtub. By this time he was about as big as a big cat, or a smallish dog, and a very pretty shiny black, like patent leather shoes.

He was getting so tame that he used to come swimming up to the top of the water and blow a fountain whenever David whistled for him.

But you can see that it wasn't very convenient to keep the whale in the bathtub, because whenever anybody wanted to take a bath, they had to bring the dish pan up from the kitchen to put the whale into, and it was hard to keep him from jumping out of the dish pan. He was so impatient to get back into the big tub where he could swim around in comfort, he simply wouldn't lie still long enough for anyone to take a bath. And every day the whale grew. By this time he was eating left-over tea biscuits, toast and vegetables. He got bigger and bigger and stronger and stronger.

At last one day David's mother said, "I simply cannot and will not be bothered lifting out this great big clumsy heavy polliwog every time anyone in this house takes a bath."

So David and his father got into the car and they drove down the hill to the Village. They went past the Grocery Store and the Butcher Store and the Drugstore and the Post Office and the Railroad Station till they came to Mister Barlow's Hardware Store.

"Good morning, Mister Barlow," said David.

"Good morning, David, fine weather we're having and what can I do for you this fine morning?" said Mister Barlow.

"I have a whale which is growing very fast, and I must have a tank to keep him in. Perhaps you keep tanks in your store?"

"Yes, indeed," said Mister Barlow proudly, and showed him several tanks. But they were goldfish tanks.

"Oh, dear no," said David, "these aren't NEARLY big enough. Show me some bigger tanks, please."

But Mister Barlow didn't have any bigger tanks. David had to order one made four times as big as the bathtub, and twice as deep and all lined with tin to make it watertight.

In two or three days the tank was finished, and Mister Barlow brought it up to David's house. They put it in the garden right beside the porch so they could watch the whale easily, and they filled it with water. It was summertime now, so the whale enjoyed living in the garden. He grew very fast from being out in the sun. He got bigger and bigger, and stronger and stronger. Pretty soon he got as big as a pony.

All the children in the neighborhood used to come to visit David's whale. They got sardines at the Grocery Store and threw them to the whale one at a time for a treat. They brought the whale ice cream cones, because whales come from the polar regions and they thought he must miss the icebergs. But the whale didn't like ice cream cones, which melted and made the water horrid and cloudy; so the children took turns changing the water in the tank with the garden hose.

One day some visitors came a long way to see the whale. There was Mister Queebus and Missis Queebus, and their little boy Alexander. They came in their car all the way from Woodstock, ninety miles away, and they were all dressed up in their Sunday-go-to-meeting clothes. They stood in a row on the porch and looked down on the whale in his tank, and admired him. The whale was so pleased with all this admiration that he blew an especially splendid fountain in honor of the Queebus family, when David whistled. It was his way of thanking them. But now he was so big that his fountain was like the smoke that you see coming out of the smokestack of a locomotive, when you sit in the car at the railroad crossing gates and watch the express go roaring by. So the fountain blew all over the Queebus family, and their best visiting clothes got soaking wet and it made them very cross.

David's mother said, "Really, we can's keep that ridiculous polliwog of David's any longer. It's MUCH too big. And I don't believe it will ever be a frog anyway!"

David was getting quite tired of changing the water in the big tank with the garden hose every few days, and of running around the Village with his red bucket, collecting bread and scraps from all the neighbors to feed the hungry whale, who ate a great deal. And the whale was growing all the time. Day by day he was getting bigger and he was getting stronger.

So David telephoned to Tony, the Express Man, to bring up his truck. And he telephoned to Nick, the Garage Man, to bring his wrecking car, and all together they hoisted the whale onto the truck by means of the derrick on the wrecking car, with wet bath towels pinned around his head to keep him from drying out on the ride.

David climbed up on the driver's seat beside Tony the Express Man, and they went down the hill to the Village. They went past the Grocery Store and past the Butcher Store and past the Drugstore and past the Post Office and past the Railroad Station till they came to Mister Barlow's Hardware Store. There David bought a very long strong chain, and then they drove the whale down to the wharf that stuck out into the river. They hooked the whale to the wharf with the chain around his tail because he hadn't any neck, and David promised to come down every day to visit him.

Every day David's father drove him down to the wharf and David whistled to the whale. The whale came up close alongside the wharf and blew lovely fountains for David.

He was a very happy and comfortable whale, swimming around the wharf and eating fresh fish right out of the river, and sleeping under the wharf at night like a dog in his kennel. He was a great pet with all the people in the Village. The Grocer brought his three little boys to see him, and the Butcher brought his little girl, and the Postman brought his twins, and the old Station Agent who sold railroad tickets for train rides brought his little golden-haired grandchild.

They all admired the whale, and some of them brought him sardines out of a can. But catching fresh fish out of the river had spoiled the whale for sardines out of a can, and he would spit them out for the crabs and fish to eat.

People used to come out from the City on Sundays just to see David's whale. The man who owned the wharf was planning to charge ten cents admission from everyone, to pay him for his trouble. But David couldn't see what trouble the man had; David took care of the whale, David had tied him up, and David had collected food for him in his bucket all the while he was growing! But all the time the whale was getting stronger and stronger.

One morning David went down to the wharf to visit the whale as usual. He whistled and whistled for the whale. But the whale didn't come to blow him a fountain. Then David noticed that the wharf was all broken at the end; planks were ripped apart, and the big heavy piles were pulled sidewise.

The whale had broken the wharf in the night. He had broken loose and had swum majestically down the river to the sea, a mighty full-grown whale, towing a piece of the chain behind him.

David went home and told his mother the whale had gone, and his mother said,

"Well, David, it was a whale after all!"

For Good Luck

Load of hay! Load of hay!
Make a wish and turn away!

Star-light, star-bright,
First star I see tonight;
I wish I may, I wish I might,
Get the wish I wish tonight.

Rain, rain, go away,
Come again another day.
Little Mary wants to play.

See a pin and pick it up,
All day long you'll have good luck;
See a pin and let it lie,
You'll want that pin before you die!

Ten Little Squirrels

Ten Little Squirrels hiding in the vine—
One leaped upon the roof, then there were nine.

Nine Little Squirrels rushing for the gate—
One found a hickory nut, then there were eight.

Eight Little Squirrels counting up to 'leven—
One got all twisted up, then there were seven.

Seven Little Squirrels in a sorry fix—
One fought an alley cat, then there were six.

Six Little Squirrels swooping in a dive—
One changed his mind, then there were five.

Five Little Squirrels round the cellar door—
One found the coal bin, then there were four.

Four Little Squirrels scolding in the tree—
One went to sleep, then there were three.

Three Little Squirrels walking in the dew—
One took a bad cold, then there were two.

Two Little Squirrels looking for some fun—
One got tired, then there was one.

One Little Squirrel hunting fame and glory—
He made a misstep, and that ends the story!

The Pirate and the Pickled Onions

By Rose Fyleman

There was once a pirate who was very fond of pickled onions. He liked them better than anything else in the world.

He was a very fierce and bold man, and each time he went out pirating he had to get a fresh crew, because he treated his men so badly that they would not go twice.

They never dared to mutiny because he always carried loaded pistols and would shoot down half a dozen men before you could say "Jack Robinson."

But he got caught in the end, and this is how it happened:

He had been on the High Seas for a month or two and had taken several ships laden with treasure, and he grew crueller and wickeder. He starved his crew and beat them and made them walk the plank if they didn't do exactly what he said almost before he said it.

And his men grew more and more annoyed, and at last determined to make an end of him. But they were terribly afraid of his pistols.

In the end they thought of a plan. The pickled onions, of which he always took a large supply, were all finished—all, that is to say, excepting one small pot which the cook kept hidden away for an occasional treat for himself, because he happened to be fond of them too.

And one night he put these onions at the bottom of a tall glass jar with an opening at the top just large enough for a man to get his hand through with a squeeze. And when the Pirate saw them on the table his eyes shone with delight, and then flashed with anger.

"Why have I not had these before?" he shouted in a rage. "Put the cook into irons at once!"

And all the crew gathered quietly around the door and waited.

Then the Pirate took a fork and began to fish about for the onions.

He liked doing that; besides if you turn a jar of them upside down all the vinegar comes out on your plate.

He ate and ate and the onions grew less and less, and at last he had to put his hand right inside the jar, squeezing it down through the neck to reach the last of the onions.

Then the little cabin-boy, who was peering through the door, gave a signal, and the whole crew rushed in and took the Pirate captive.

You see, he couldn't get his hand out quickly enough to get at his pistols, and when he lifted up the pickle jar and tried to hit out with that, the vinegar ran down into his eyes so that he couldn't even see.

And they fastened him up in a sack and threw him into the sea and that was the end of him.

But the crew came home with all the treasure and were rich men for the rest of their lives.

A Riddle

Thirty white horses upon a red hill:
Now they tramp, now they clamp,
Now they stand still.

Teeth and gums

The Three Bears

Once there were Three Bears who lived in a nice little house in the woods. There were lots of flowers in bloom all around the house, and in the back yard there was a perfectly enormous bee-hive, because as you know bees love honey.

Father Bear was called Big Bear. He was very big and strong, and he had a deep gruff voice that rumbled when he talked. Mother Bear was not quite so big—she was Middle-Sized Bear—and she had a high voice that was a little shrill when she was excited. Baby Bear was little, and he had a little squeaky voice. Everybody called him Little Bear.

The Three Bears liked to do everything together, and one fine morning after Middle-Sized Bear had made the beds and cooked the porridge for breakfast, they decided to go for a little walk in the woods while the porridge was cooling. Big Bear and Little Bear waited on the doorstep while Middle-Sized Bear hurried back into the house to stir some more honey into Little Bear's porridge,

38

because Little Bear liked his porridge very, very sweet. Soon she came out, and they walked into the woods, Big Bear and Middle-Sized Bear with Little Bear between them.

Just then a little girl who shouldn't have wandered so far from home by herself came up to the Bears' house. She had long yellow curls, and everybody called her Goldilocks. She was a spoilt little brat, as you will see for yourself. She did not know who lived in that nice little house, but she was tired and thirsty, and she thought she would knock on the door and ask the people for a drink of water. She knocked and of course nobody answered, because the Bears were out walking. She shouldn't have opened the door and walked in, but she did; and the first thing she saw was the steaming porridge set out in three bowls on the table. She shouldn't have touched the porridge, but she did.

She tasted Big Bear's porridge and it burned her mouth, so she threw the spoon down and tasted Middle-Sized Bear's porridge. That was also too hot, and she didn't like the flavor. Then she saw Little Bear's bowl, and his porridge had cooled faster than the others' had because there was less of it. It was very, very sweet, and Goldilocks thought it was delicious. Before you could count to ten

she had eaten every bit of it and scraped the bowl.

She looked around and saw a tall, big chair, and she climbed into it. It was Big Bear's chair, and it was strong and hard and even the cushions were big and hard and heavy. Goldilocks kicked the cushions around (which she shouldn't have done) but they were hard any way she turned them, so she got down and tried the next chair, which was Middle-Sized Bear's. That was big and soft; the cushions were soft and sort of smothery. That chair didn't please her, but then she saw Little Bear's little chair, and that was just right for her. She liked it so much and bounced up and down so many times that the bottom fell out!

Goldilocks pulled herself out of the broken chair, and without looking to see if she could put it together again (which she should have done) she ran upstairs (which she shouldn't have done) and climbed onto the first bed she saw. It was Big Bear's bed and it was big and strong and hard, and of course she didn't like it. So she got down, leaving the bed all mussed up, and went to the next.

41

bed, which belonged to Middle-Sized Bear, and was not quite so big. It was softer, but not soft enough and too big for her, so she got down and went to Little Bear's bed. That was just right, and she curled up and went to sleep.

Soon Big Bear, Middle-Sized Bear and Little Bear came in, and went to the table to eat their breakfast.

"Somebody's been tasting my porridge!" rumbled Big Bear, in his big, gruff voice.

"Somebody's been tasting my porridge!" said Middle-Sized Bear, in her high shrill voice.

"Somebody's eaten up all my porridge!" wailed Little Bear, in his funny squeaky voice.

Somebody certainly had, and the Bears decided to sit down and talk it over.

"Somebody's been sitting in my chair!" rumbled Big Bear in his big, gruff voice.

"Somebody's been sitting in my chair!" said Middle-Sized Bear, in her high shrill voice.

"Somebody's been sitting in my chair, and has broken it all to pieces!" wailed Little Bear, in his funny squeaky voice.

Then the Three Bears went upstairs.

"Somebody's been on my bed!" rumbled Big Bear in his big, gruff voice.

"Somebody's been on my bed!" said Middle-Sized Bear in her high shrill voice.

"Somebody's in my bed right now!" Little Bear tried to shout the news, but his voice sounded funnier and more squeaky than ever.

The Three Bears stood by Little Bear's bed and looked at Goldilocks. She had heard the voices, like noises far away, in her sleep; and now with three pairs of astonished eyes looking at her, she opened her own eyes. She saw Big Bear, and he looked very, very big; she saw Middle-Sized Bear, and she looked big and sort of fierce; she saw Little Bear, and some other time she might have liked to play with him—but not just then. Goldilocks was scared (which served her right). The window was open, and it took her just one second to jump out of it. It took another second for her to pick herself up, and by the time the Three Bears got over to the window they saw her running like mad down the path away from the woods.

And that is all that anybody knows about it.

The Ice-Cream Man

By Rachel Field

When summer's in the city,
　　And brick's a blaze of heat,
The Ice-cream Man with his little cart
　　Goes trundling down the street.

Beneath his round umbrella,
　　Oh, what a joyful sight,
To see him fill the cones with mounds
　　Of cooling brown or white:

Vanilla, chocolate, strawberry,
　　Or chilly things to drink
From bottles full of frosty-fizz,
　　Green, orange, white or pink.

His cart might be a flower bed
　　Of roses and sweet peas,
The way the children cluster round
　　As thick as honeybees.

A Strange Little Home

By Alice Gall and Fleming Crew

One pleasant afternoon in early summer three young chipmunks were sitting on an old fallen tree in the forest, chattering together about the exciting things that were always going on in the world around them. They had been digging for grubs and beetles in the soft earth under the fallen tree, for grubs and beetles are good food, young chipmunks think.

"Mother says there will soon be plenty of seeds and ripe berries for us to eat," one of the little chipmunks was saying. "And then we won't have to dig for grubs any more."

"I like to dig," spoke up another.

"So do I," the third chipmunk said. "I can hardly wait until it is time for us to dig our burrows. Won't it be fun having burrows all our very own?"

"We won't have them for a long time yet," the first chipmunk

46

reminded him. "Mother says we will have to learn a great deal more about the ways of the forest before we are ready for homes of our own. She says—"

He stopped short. "Look!" he exclaimed in a startled voice. "Look down there by the old stump!"

The other little chipmunks looked, and saw a sight so strange that for a moment the three of them could only sit there staring at it in amazement. A queer creature was coming slowly along the hillside, and it seemed to be headed straight for the old fallen tree.

It did not have a furry body like theirs. It seemed to have no body at all, and looked like a round humped stone that was crawling along the ground. But it had legs, very short and stubby ones, and it had a head and a long slim neck.

"What can it be?" one of the chipmunks asked breathlessly. "It may be unfriendly. We'd better hurry home to our burrow."

"It is too slow to be dangerous," said another. "Look, you can

scarcely see it move. It could never catch us."

As the creature drew nearer the little chipmunks could see that the humped stone was really a shell, beautifully marked with spots of yellow and black. "I'm not afraid of it," one of the chipmunks boasted, and calling out in a loud voice he asked: "Are you a friendly creature, or are you unfriendly?"

The voice that answered them was so small and thin that the little chipmunks could scarcely hear it. "Friendly," it said. "I am a friendly old land turtle, and will harm no one."

"We are young chipmunks," they announced, when the turtle had reached the fallen tree.

"I know you are," the turtle said. "I have seen young chipmunks before, and you all look just alike. You all have brown fur, and you all have black stripes down your backs, and you all have bushy tails. Where do you live, Young Chipmunks?"

"In a burrow, here on the hillside," one of them answered.

"Where do you live, Old Turtle? Have you a burrow in the forest somewhere?"

"Turtles do not live in burrows," he told them.

"Do you live in a nest then?" they asked. "Or in some cave or hollow log?"

"No, I do not live in any of those places," the turtle replied. "But I have a home, and a very good one too. It is safer than a burrow, and snugger than a nest. My shell is my home, Young Chipmunks, and since it is fastened to me, I take it with me wherever I go. It has a hard roof above and a hard floor below. And when I want to, I can shut myself in so securely that no unfriendly creature can reach me, no matter how hard it may try."

"Let's see you shut yourself in, Old Turtle," the little chipmunks cried.

"Very well," the turtle said, and at once he began to draw himself into his shell. Little by little he disappeared—his head, his legs and even his tail—until none of the turtle was left outside.

The surprised young chipmunks looked first at the shell and then at each other. And they were very glad when, presently, the old turtle poked his head out again.

"We thought you were gone for good!" they cried. What became of you?"

"I only went inside my home and closed my door," the old turtle told them. And now he raised himself a little on his stubby legs and started to waddle slowly off down the hillside.

"Good day, Young Chipmunks," he called back to them. "I hope we shall see each other often before the summer is over."

And the little chipmunks hoped so too.

My Steam Shovel

By Vera Edelstadt

I like steam boats and tugs, steam engines and dredges, steam rollers and calliopes, but best of all I love Steam Shovels.

I watch them when they are digging great holes in the ground. Holes as big as mountains pretty near, but going the wrong way—going down, not up, and cutting earth instead of sky.

Did you ever watch a steam shovel? It's not much like a shovel that you use on the sand—that you hold in your hand to dig. It's big. Big as a giant's. And it moves so slow you can see it go swinging from the hole to the truck where it dumps the dirt.

I've got to shovel with a plain shovel now. But when I grow up I'd like to shovel with a Steam Shovel!

I'd like to stand in the cabin, with my hands on the levers, and shovel!

I'd pull one, and my cabin would turn around on a round track. I'd pull another, and the "grab" would swing into place. I'd pull another, and the fist would open wide, and grab at the earth.

And all the time the steam would puff softly in the chimney overhead.

Then I'd pull another lever and the steam would growl, "get 'em up! get 'em up!" and pull the "grab" out of the dirt, to the truck, to drop the load.

When the steam didn't have much power, I'd open a little door where the embers glowed, and put some more wood on the fire, to heat the water and to make more steam.

And then I'd pull the levers again. And go riding in a circle in the cabin of the Steam Shovel.

Cinderella

Once there was a girl who was as sweet and kind as she was beautiful; but she was obliged to live with two cross sisters who made her work very hard all day long, and every day. They called her Cinderella because in the evening, when her other work was done, she would sit in the chimney corner and rake the cinders.

The sisters had beautiful big bedrooms, with full length mirrors and handsome furniture; but Cindrella's room was the attic and she slept on a bed of straw with one ragged blanket to cover her. The sisters had many beautiful dresses and dazzling jewels, and they were always choosing new ones, but Cinderella had to dress in coarse rags. While the sisters sat all day before their mirrors, thinking up new ways to arrange their hair, Cinderella had to cook the meals, wash the dishes and scrub the floors. If she stopped to rest for a few minutes the sisters scolded her.

One day the sisters received invitations to a ball at the palace, and they were so excited that they could neither eat nor sleep. They were sure it would be a very splendid affair, and perhaps the handsome Prince would ask them to dance! What should they wear? What was really the most becoming style to arrange their hair? They asked Cinderella's advice, because they knew that her taste was much better than theirs.

At last the great day came, and Cinderella was busy helping them dress, taking a stitch here, and pressing a fold there.

"How would you like to go to the ball?" one of the sisters asked her.

"Of course I would like to go," answered Cinderella, "but I have nothing fit to wear. "They would not let me come in these clothes."

The sister laughed in a very unpleasant way, and said, "At least you know that a ball at the palace is no place for a poor ragged thing like you!"

When the coach which the sisters had hired to take them to the ball was at the door, they came down grumbling because they said they would be much handsomer if they had worn other dresses!

When poor Cinderella sat down on her stool by the kitchen fire she was so tired and so unhappy that she began to cry.

"What does this mean?" asked a sweet voice at her side. "You should be at the ball, child! Why do you sit here moping?"

Cinderella looked up in astonishment, and saw the most exquisite little woman she had ever laid her eyes on standing at the other side of the chimney.

"Oh, ma'm," she said, "I do wish I could go to the ball, but the

sisters said it was no place for a poor ragged thing like me!"

"Well, we shall see about that!" said the fairy, for it was a fairy, Cinderella's own fairy godmother. "Have you any pumpkins in the garden, my dear?"

That seemed an odd question, but Cinderella answered sweetly, "Yes, ma'm, we have several, and one that is very big."

"Go and pick the big one, and bring it to the front door," she was told.

The garden was bright in the moonlight, and Cinderella quickly found the pumpkin and brought it to the door.

The fairy touched it with her wand, and instantly it became a large and comfortable coach, covered with gold decorations. "I hope there are some mice in that trap in the pantry," said the fairy. "Go and see."

Sure enough there were six fat mice in the trap, and the fairy told Cinderella to let them out slowly, one by one. As each one hopped out she turned it into a spirited horse, and in a moment the horses were harnessed to the coach.

"Now," said the fairy, "see if you can find a rat or two in that trap in the cellar."

There were three rats, and the fairy chose the biggest one and turned him into a coachman. Then she sent Cinderella to look behind the watering can in the garden for six lizards. These she turned into footmen, dressed in bottle green, with many brass buttons. They took their places and waited.

"Now you can go to the ball," said the fairy.

"Oh, ma'm, surely not in these clothes!" said Cinderella.

Then the fairy touched Cinderella's rags with her wand, chang-

ing them into the most beautiful ball dress imaginable. Jewels
sparkled at her throat and in her hair. From her pocket the fairy
took a pair of dainty glass slippers, and when Cinderella slipped
them on they fitted her tiny feet perfectly.

"Have a good time, my dear," said the fairy, "but remember
this: my power lasts only until midnight. See to it that you are back
by that time, for on the stroke of twelve your coach will become a
common pumpkin again, your servants and horses small animals,
and your fine gown nothing but rags. Do not forget this."

When Cinderella arrived at the ball she was by far the most
beautiful girl in the room. She told no one her name, and everybody thought she was a princess from some rich and distant
country. The King and Queen were delighted with her beauty
and her charming manners; and from the moment that she entered

the room the handsome Prince had no eyes for anyone else. He danced with her, and took her in to supper, bringing her quantities of the rarest and most choice food. This she made a point of sharing with the sisters who she could see were sadly neglected.

At a quarter to twelve Cinderella said good-by very charmingly to everyone and left hastily. The Prince himself put her into her coach, imploring her to stay all evening, or at least for the next dance.

When Cinderella reached home, just as the clock struck twelve, her godmother smiled and asked her if she had enjoyed the ball. Of course she had, and now it was such fun to tell the fairy all about it!

Her coach was in the garden, again a big pumpkin; her servants and horses were back where they came from in their former shapes, and she herself was once more in rags. But she still had the glass slippers, and the fairy told her to put them away where no one else could find them.

All too soon a coach rumbled up to the door, and Cinderella heard the sisters' voices. At once the fairy vanished, and Cinderella went to the door yawning, as though she had been sound asleep.

While she was helping the sisters undress they told her about the beautiful and richly dressed princess who had come from no one knew where, and had left long before the ball was over. "She was particularly kind to us," they said, "and it was quite plain to everyone that the Prince fell head over heels in love with her. He doesn't even know her name, because she would tell no one, but the Prince is giving another ball tomorrow night, hoping that she will return."

"How I would love to see her," said Cinderella. "Wouldn't you lend me one of your oldest dresses so that I could go tomorrow night and see this lovely princess?"

The sisters who had been chatting rather pleasantly now became cross, and told her that she wouldn't know how to behave at a ball; that she must be out of her mind to think of such a thing! Of course they would not let her wear anything of theirs —the very idea!

Cinderella was smiling quietly to herself all the time. She had known that they would say something like that.

The next day Cinderella had a harder time than before getting the sisters dressed to their liking, and they were crosser than ever; but at last they left the house in their hired coach, and even before Cinderella had time to sit down there was her fairy godmother;

and in less time than it takes to tell it the coach, coachman, horses and footmen were at the door, and Cinderella was dressed even more gorgeously than before. She stepped into her glass slippers and was ready to go.

"Remember," said the fairy, "if you are not back by midnight I told you what would happen, and it will be your own fault, for I cannot help you after twelve o'clock."

Tonight the ball was even more splendid; and the Prince, even more fascinated by Cinderella's beauty and charm, never once left her side. The child was having such a good time that she never once thought of looking at the clock until it was just three seconds to twelve! She ran as fast as she could out of the ballroom and into the great hall, but before she could run down the palace steps her fine gown and jewels had vanished. She looked like a beggar in rags. She saw six little gray mice, one big gray rat and six green lizards running into the shrubbery, and on the drive at the foot of the steps lay a large yellow pumpkin!

Even in her distress she giggled at the sight of it, but she wanted to cry when she found that she had lost one of her precious glass slippers. She had no idea where she had dropped it, and did not dare to go back to look for it, for already she could hear voices calling and feet pounding on the drive behind her. The light from many torches pierced the darkness, as the guests joined the servants in the search for the lovely princess who had vanished so strangely.

It seemed a long, weary way home, and when she arrived her fairy godmother looked at her sternly, but they had no time to talk

because the sisters' coach rolled up immediately, and the fairy vanished.

The sisters were very much excited, and they told Cinderella how the fair princess had run out of the ballroom with the Prince close behind her, and how distressed he was when no trace of her could be found. They said he found one of her exquisite glass slippers and picked it up, but nobody had seen which way she went. Even the gatekeeper said that no one had gone out except a poor ragged beggar girl, and that was very strange because the lady's fine coach, with its footmen and horses were gone too. Now where could that coach have got to? No one could find a trace of it, they said.

Cinderella was unhooking a gown just then, and she had to duck her head quickly. She couldn't help smiling when she remembered the pumpkin lying at the bottom of the palace steps.

The next week the King's Chamberlain, richly dressed in scarlet and gold, marched through the town. A page with a trumpet called everyone to attention. Another page carried a velvet cushion on which lay the glass slipper that the Prince had found on the palace steps. The Prince, frantic to find the lovely lady so that he could marry her at once, begged that every girl in the kingdom would try on the slipper. He promised to marry the one who could wear it, for he was very sure that it would fit no one but its rightful owner.

Of course the sisters tried their very best to squeeze their big feet into it, but they couldn't. Then Cinderella asked if she might try. The sisters spoke sharply, and told her to get back to her scrubbing; but the haughty Chamberlain smiled and said of course she might try, that it was every maiden's privilege.

When Cinderella put her dainty foot into the slipper everyone could see at once that it fitted her to perfection; and they were greatly astonished when she took its mate from her pocket and slipped it on the other foot. Just then the fairy appeared and changed Cinderella's rags into the richest costume that had ever been seen in all the land, with jewels richer and more sparkling than before.

The sisters fell on their knees before her and asked her forgiveness of all their unkindness, and Cinderella very sweetly told them that she had already forgiven them. The King sent his best state coach to bring Cinderella to the palace. Within a few days she and the Prince were married, and they lived happily ever after.

The Swing

By Robert Louis Stevenson

How do you like to go up in a swing,
  Up in the air so blue?
Oh, I do think it's the pleasantest thing
  Ever a child can do!

Up in the air and over the wall,
  Till I can see so wide,
Rivers and trees and cattle and all
  Over the countryside—

Till I look down on the garden green,
  Down on the roof so brown—
Up in the air I go flying again,
  Up in the air and down!

Mr. Easter Rabbit

By Carolyn Sherwin Bailey

A long time ago, in a far-off country, there was a famine; and this is how it came about:

In the early spring when the grass first peeped out, the sun shone so hot that the grass was dried up. No rains fell through the long summer months, so that the seed and grain that were planted could not grow, and everywhere the fields and meadows—usually so green and rich—were a dull gray-brown.

Here and there a green tree waved its dusty branches in the hot wind. When fall came, instead of the well-filled granaries and barns, there was great emptiness; and instead of happy fathers and mothers, there were grave, troubled ones.

But the children were just as happy as ever. They were glad, even, that it had not rained, for they could play out of doors all day long; and the dust-piles had never been so large and fine.

The people had to be very saving of the things that had been left from the year before. All the following winter, by being very careful, they managed to provide simple food for their families. When Christmas came there were not many presents, but the children did not miss them as we would, because in that land they did not give many presents at Christmas-time.

Their holiday was Easter Sunday. On that day they had a great celebration, and there were always goodies and presents for the little boys and girls. As the time came nearer, the parents wondered what they should do for the children's holiday. Every new day it was harder than the day before to get just plain, coarse bread to eat; and where would they find all the sweetmeats and pretty things that the children had always had at Easter-time?

One evening some of the mothers met, after the children were in bed, to talk about what they should do. One mother said, "We can have eggs. All the chickens are laying; but the children are so tired of eggs, for they have them every day."

So they decided that eggs would never do for an Easter treat; and they went home sorrowfully, thinking that Easter must come and go like any other day. And one mother was more sorry than any of the others. Her dear little boy and girl had been planning and talking about the beautiful time they were going to have on the great holiday.

After the mother had gone to bed, she wondered and thought if there were any way by which she could give her little ones their happy time. All at once she cried right out in the dark:

"I know! I have thought of something to make the children happy!"

She could hardly wait until morning, and the first thing she did was to run into the next house and tell her neighbor of the bright plan she had thought of. And the neighbor told someone else, and so the secret flew until, before night, all the mothers had heard it, but not a single child.

There was still a week before Easter, so there was a good deal of whispering; and the fathers and mothers smiled every time they thought of the secret.

When Easter Sunday came every one went, first of all, to the great stone church—mothers and fathers and children. When church was over, instead of going home, the older people suggested walking to the great woods just back of the church.

"Perhaps we may find some flowers," they said.

So on they went, and soon the merry children were scattered through the woods, among the trees. Then a shout went up—now here, now there—from all sides.

"Father, mother, look here!"

"See what I have found—some beautiful eggs!"

"Here's a red one!"

"I've found a yellow one!"

"Here's a whole nestful—all different colors."

And the children came running, bringing beautiful colored eggs which they had found in the soft moss under the trees. What kind of eggs could they be? They were too large for birds' eggs; they were large, like hens' eggs; but who ever saw a hen's egg so wonderfully colored?

Just then, from behind a large tree, where the children had found a nest full of eggs, there jumped a rabbit, and with long

leaps he disappeared in the deep woods, where he was hidden from view by the trees and bushes.

"It must be that the rabbit laid the pretty eggs," said one little girl.

"I am sure it was the rabbit," said her mother.

"Hurrah for the rabbit! Hurrah for the Easter rabbit! Hurrah for Mr. Easter Rabbit!" the children cried; and the fathers and mothers were glad with the children.

So this is the story of the first Easter eggs, for, ever since then, in that far-away land and in other countries too, has Mr. Easter Rabbit brought the children at Easter-time some beautiful colored eggs.

A Riddle

Little Nancy Etticoat
In a white petticoat
And a red rose.
The longer she stands,
The shorter she grows.

A Candle

The Lamb

By William Blake

Little Lamb, who made thee?
Dost thou know who made thee?

Gave thee life and bid thee feed,
By the stream and o'er the mead;
Gave thee clothing of delight,
Softest clothing, woolly, bright;
Gave thee such a tender voice,
Making all the vales rejoice?

Little Lamb, who made thee?
Dost thou know who made thee?

Little Lamb, I'll tell thee:
Little Lamb, I'll tell thee:

He is called by thy name,
For He calls Himself a lamb,
He is meek and He is mild;
He became a little child.
I a child, and thou a lamb,
We are called by His name.

Little Lamb, God bless thee!
Little Lamb, God bless thee!

Names

By Dorothy Aldis

Larkspur and Hollyhock,
Pink Rose and purple Stock,
Lovely smiling Mignonette,
Lilies not quite opened yet,
Phlox the favorite of bees,
Bleeding Heart and Peonies—
Just their names are nice to say,
Softly,
On a summer's day.

The Little Boy Who Wouldn't Get Up

By Rose Fyleman

There was once a dreadfully lazy little boy who would not get up in the morning.

They used to come time after time to waken him up, but he would just turn over and go to sleep again. Very often they had to pull him right out of bed, and even then he sometimes used to go to sleep on the floor. It was very tiresome and vexatious.

And one day everyone was very busy, and they came out once or twice to call him and then forgot all about him. And he slipped right down into the bed between the sheets, so that nothing of him was to be seen, and slept on and on.

It was the day the laundry sent for the washing.

The maid came upstairs to get the sheets to send with the other things. And she bundled the little boy up with the sheets without noticing; and he was put into the hamper with all the other things and sent to the wash.

And he was thrown into the water at the laundry and boiled until he was all red, and then he was soaped until he was all white, and then he was stirred round and round until he was all blue, and then he was mangled until he was as thin as a piece of blotting paper, and then he was dried until he was all wrinkly, and then he was starched until he was as hard as a kipper, and then he was ironed until he was as stiff as a poker, and then he was folded neatly and packed up between sheets of blue tissue paper and entered in the laundry book as:

Boy 1

and then he was sent home. They were very much astonished to see him, as you may imagine.

It took him a long, long time to get over all this, but it cured him of getting up so late in the morning. He jumps up the minute he's called now.

I'm not sure that this is quite a true tale. I do hope you don't mind.

Specky and Her Family

Specky was a nice fat hen. She lived with some other hens and a rooster in Mrs. Smith's henhouse.

One spring after Specky had laid a great many nice eggs, oh! twenty-five or thirty maybe, one every day for twenty-five or thirty days, she decided that it was time for her to stop laying eggs for a while, and she thought it would be nice to have a family of fluffy, downy, yellow chicks. So she began ruffling her feathers and clucking, and clucking and ruffling her feathers so that Mrs. Smith would know how she felt about it. She did it all day long.

"Joe," said Mrs. Smith to her husband that night, "Specky has stopped laying, and she is going around clucking and ruffling her feathers, but we don't need any more little chicks. I thought I might let her sit on those duck eggs that John Dixon traded you for that little runty pig. The pond is near enough for them to swim on, and I think we would like duck to eat next winter."

"Do it," said Mr. Smith, with a chuckle. "Old Lady Specky will be surprised when she sees what she hatches!"

So bright and early the next morning Mrs. Smith made a nest for Specky out of clean, fresh straw, and put twelve duck eggs in it. Then she caught Specky and put her in the nest and turned a basket over her, so that she would not wander off.

Specky clucked and fussed and pecked at the eggs, trying to get them settled comfortably under her. They were very big eggs, but Specky did not mind. She would take good care of them, and maybe she would have very big chicks.

But Specky did mind when those eggs did not hatch when she thought they should. She knew well enough—but don't ask me how she knew—that she must sit for three weeks on hen eggs before they would hatch; but of course she didn't know that she was sitting on duck eggs, and that duck eggs take four weeks to hatch. That last week was very long and tiresome to poor Specky.

When the little ducklings began to come out of their shells Specky was very much astonished to see how funny they looked! It is true they were as fluffy and yellow and as downy as any mother hen could wish, but what funny bills they had, and what very funny feet! No matter; they were her own children; they were big and strong, and she was very proud of them!

They waddled in a queer way when they went to get their breakfast of soft dough that Mrs. Smith brought out from the kitchen, and they spooned up their food with their tiny bills in a very funny way, but Specky, like a good mother hen, saw to it that they all ate heartily before she ate her own breakfast.

The next day and the next the ducklings became more and more restless. Specky did not understand it at all. They seemed to want something, and to want it very badly, but surely they had everything that good little chicks could want. They had a devoted mother, a nice clean coop to live in, plenty of food to eat and water to drink in a shiny pan that was not too deep. What more could they want?

The first fine warm morning Mrs. Smith let Specky take her family out of the chicken yard for a little walk. They had no sooner got outside the gate than the little ducklings began to waddle like

mad down towards the pond! Specky clucked and clucked and showed them some very special worms, but nothing she could do would stop them. So she ran after them, and wasn't she astonished and scared, too, when every last one of her children got right into the water, and paddled away with their funny little feet!

They made a very pretty sight, with their little heads held high, and their feet making tiny ripples on the water, but poor Specky did not notice that. She ran with her wings outspread, clucking and squawking, up and down by the side of the pond, but those naughty children paid no attention to her calls!

Of course it never occurred to the ducklings that their poor, frantic mother thought they were all going to drown. They were having a wonderful time, and when they finished their swim they came back to their mother. She clucked and started back to their coop, and they came very obediently.

The next day and the next they went back to the pond. Perhaps they made Specky understand that they simply had to swim, because she got used to her queer family and became very proud of them. She had a family that could do something that none of the other hens' children could do!

The next summer Mrs. Smith gave Specky hen eggs to sit on, and when they hatched they were fluffy, downy yellow chicks exactly like those the other hens had.

And what do you suppose Specky did? When they were old enough to go to walk she took them straight to the pond, and tried her very best to push them in! Of course they did not understand why their mother, who had been so good to them, wanted to push them into the cold water. One or two of them got wet and cold and very unhappy, but the others wisely ran away and wouldn't go near the horrid place! Specky was puzzled, and she didn't like it one bit.

That night she left her family all alone, and flew up on the roost to sleep with the other hens. Mrs. Smith had to take Specky's little chicks and put them in a box behind the kitchen stove. She had to cover them up at night, and take care of them herself. Specky never looked at them again. She would have nothing to do with a family who would not swim!

Valentine to My Mother

By Christina Rossetti

All the Robin Redbreasts
    Have lived the winter through,
Jenny Wrens have pecked their fill
    And found a work to do;
Families of Sparrows
    Have weathered wind and storm
With Rabbit on the stony hill
    And Hare upon her form.

You and I, my Mother
    Have lived the winter through,
And still we play our daily parts
    And still find work to do:
And still you reign my Queen of Hearts
    And I'm your Valentine.

Puss in Boots

Once there was a miller who had three sons. He had a mill, an ass and a cat. When the miller died, the eldest son took the mill, the middle son took the ass, and that left nothing but the cat for the youngest son.

The youngest son was very sad. He did not know how he could make a living with only a big striped cat to help him. But the cat came and rubbed against his legs, and said: "Master, I think we may do very well indeed if you will give me a good stout bag with a cord to draw it close, and buy me a pair of good, high boots."

The young man was very much surprised. He had not known that his cat was such a smart animal. He went to the mill and got a bag which he gave to Puss, and then went to town and bought a pair of boots.

When he returned Puss drew the boots on his hind legs, took the bag in his mouth, and went at once to a thicket where he knew there were many rabbits. But first he filled his bag with tender green leaves and a carrot or two to tempt the rabbits. He lay down nearby to wait, and it was not long before a foolish young rabbit dashed into the bag. Puss quickly closed the bag, strangled the rabbit, and picked up the bag. He went to the palace and asked to see the king.

The king was wearing his everyday crown, and he did not seem pleased to have a visitor; but when the cat spoke to him very respectfully, and begged him to receive a bit of game which he had brought from his master, the Marquis of Carabas, the king smiled, and accepted the gift with suitable thanks.

Of course neither the king nor anyone else had ever heard of the Marquis of Carabas. Puss had just thought up that high-sounding title, but Puss, being a shrewd animal, was sure that no one would ask questions, and no one did.

Two or three times a week Puss went to the palace with a present of game for the king. Sometimes it would be quail, or nice fat partridges, and other times a nice fat rabbit. He always said that the present was sent by his master, the Marquis of Carabas, the famous sportsman.

One day, after this had been going on for sometime, Puss heard that the king was going for a drive by the river. His daughter, a very beautiful princess was going with him.

Puss rushed home and told his master that their fortunes were made if he would do exactly as Puss told him. The young man agreed, and Puss told him to go and bathe in the river at a particular spot, and leave everything else to him. As soon as the young man

had thrown off his clothes and jumped in the river, Puss hid the clothes which were old and faded, where no one else could find them. Then hearing the rumbling of wheels, he rushed out into the road and threw up his front paws just as the king's coach drove up. Yes, the king was inside, looking out of one window, and the beautiful princess was looking out of the other.

"Help, help!" Puss cried, "my dear master, the famous Marquis of Carabas is drowning! Oh, help him, help him, kind sir, whoever you may be!"

(That sly puss knew perfectly well who it was!)

Of course the king recognized Puss. No other cat went around dressed in high boots, giving away game, so he sent three of his strongest men to rescue the Marquis of Carabas. Puss thanked him very prettily for his goodness, and then said with a deep sigh:

"Unfortunately my master, the Marquis of Carabas, will not be able to thank you and the princess himself for the great favor you have done him. His clothes were stolen by a thief while he was in bathing, and I was not able to catch him."

The king called one of his outriders, and told the man to gallop to the palace, and bring one of his richest warmest robes to lend to the Marquis of Carabas. "Hurry," said the king, "or the poor marquis will have a chill!"

As soon as the man returned Puss's master threw the robe around him, and came to the coach to pay his respects to the king. He was a tall, handsome young man, with blue eyes and a nice smile, and the rich robe made him look every inch a marquis. The king was very much impressed with the young man's good looks and easy manner of speaking, and the princess was even more impressed. She fell in love with him without a moment's delay.

The king invited the Marquis of Carabas to ride with them in the coach, and Puss, delighted at the way his plans were working out, ran ahead on business of his own.

He came to a meadow where men were mowing the hay. "Friends," he said to them, "the king will soon pass this way, and if he stops and asks you who owns this meadow, say it belongs to the Marquis of Carabas. If you do not say this you will be cut into small pieces!" Puss stamped his boot angrily, and went on.

When Puss found reapers in a corn field along the road he told them the same thing. Then he stamped his boot and went on.

He repeated this to every group of laborers he saw along the roadside. Then he would stamp his boot and run on.

At last he came to a magnificent castle, where a wicked ogre lived. The ogre was very, very rich. All the fields that Puss had passed belong to him.

Puss knocked boldly on the castle door, and told the doorman

that he had come a long way to pay his respects to his master, and hoped that the master would be so kind as to receive him. The ogre agreed to see Puss for a moment or two.

Puss told the ogre that he had passed through his lands, and knew that he was rich and very powerful. Puss said he had heard that the ogre could turn himself into any animal, such as a lion or an elephant. The ogre said of course he could, and he would prove it by changing himself into a lion. He did, and roared most frightfully. Puss, pretending to be much alarmed, climbed up on the roof. With his heavy boots on this was very difficult, but Puss believed in safety first.

When the ogre changed back into his natural shape, Puss came down, and looked with admiration at his host.

"I should not have doubted," he said, "that you could change into a lion, for you are the greatest and most powerful of ogres. You have the heart of a lion, so it is perhaps not really hard for you to take his shape. Forgive me, please, when I say that I am sure you could not become a rat, or anything as weak and contemptible as a mouse!"

"So you are sure I can't become a mouse, are you?" said the ogre, "I'll show you."

Then—puff!—the ogre was gone, and a tiny mouse frisked about the floor. Puss pounced on the mouse and killed him, and that was the end of the ogre.

Puss took over the castle at once in the name of his master, the Marquis of Carabas. He told all the servants that the master was coming with the king and the princess, and ordered them to prepare a royal feast.

Meanwhile the king's coach was rolling along the road, and just as Puss had thought, the king stopped and asked all the laborers he saw whose lands they were working. They all told him that the lands and the crops belonged to the Marquis of Carabas. The king was very much impressed, and Puss's master said quietly that his land was not bad, and his crops brought him a fair income.

When they reached the driveway to the ogre's castle there was Puss, bowing and smiling. He called out:

"Welcome, your majesty, and your royal highness, to the castle of the Marquis of Carabas. We hope that you will come in and refresh yourselves after your long drive."

A few weeks later there was a fine wedding at the palace. The beautiful princess became the wife of the rich and handsome Marquis of Carabas, and went to live at his magnificent castle.

Puss, who had served his master well, put aside his boots which were rather uncomfortable. He lived in ease on the fat of the land for the rest of his life, only chasing a mouse for exercise.

The Dog and his Shadow

One day a dog was trotting down the road with a nice juicy piece of meat in his mouth. He was crossing a stream on a footbridge when he looked into the water and saw what he thought was another dog with a much bigger piece of meat in his mouth.

The dog dropped his meat and jumped into the water to take the bigger piece of meat away from the other dog. Of course what he had seen was just his own shadow reflected in the water when he had looked down. Meanwhile his own piece of meat had fallen off the bridge into the water. It sank to the bottom of the stream, and he never saw it again.

The dog had to go without dinner that day unless he had a bone buried somewhere, or had a bit of luck hunting.

Do you think he may have learned a good lesson—that it never pays to be greedy?

Counting-Out Rhyme

Icker-backer,
Silver cracker,
Icker-backer-boo.
    En-gine
    Number Nine,
Out go you.

Out goes the cat,
Out goes the rat,
Out goes the lady
    In the see-saw hat.

O-U-T spells Out,
So go!

How the Little Owl's Name Was Changed

By Charles E. Gillham

Every spring in Alaska a little owl would come north with the other birds. It was only a tiny owl and flew noiselessly over the tundra on its soft, downy wings. At first the Eskimos called him Anipausigak, which means "the little owl." Later, after the Eskimos knew more about the bird, they called him Kerayule, which means in their language "the owl that makes no noise when he flies."

In the very early days, before the white men came to Alaska, the Eskimos had no matches and it was very difficult for them to have a fire. Also there was very little wood in the Eskimo country.

One spring there was one family, living all by themselves, that had a bit of fire but there was no place where they could get any if this went out. In the middle of the igloo was a pit, or hole, in the

floor. Here a tiny little bit of fire was kept burning at all times. Always someone watched it and tended it. The smoke went curling out of the window in the top of the igloo.

In this igloo there were a little boy and a little girl with their father and mother. All times of the day and night someone had to stay in the house and watch the tiny fire. One day when the little girl was all alone—her folks were out hunting seals—some bad people came to the igloo.

"Oh, so you are all alone, little girl," one of them said. "I suppose you are watching the fire so that it does not go out?"

"Yes," said the little girl. "It would be very bad if we lost our fire. We would be very cold, and would have nothing to cook by. I must watch it carefully so that when my parents come home there will be a warm house here to greet them."

The bad man laughed. "You will not have to watch your fire any more, little girl, for we have no fire in our igloo and we are going to take yours with us."

How frightened the little girl was, and how badly she felt to think she was going to lose the fire! She thought quickly. "Can't I make you some fire on another stick, Mr. Man?" she asked. "Then you can take it with you and I will still have some left for my mother and father and my little brother when they come home from hunting seals."

"I haven't time to wait for you to make new fire," the bad man said, "and, besides, I do not care if you are cold and hungry." With that he grabbed the fire and went away with it, leaving the poor little girl crying and all her fire gone.

When the mother and father and little brother came home they

98

found the igloo cold, and the little girl told them what had happened. Hastily the father took his bow and arrow and set out to the igloo of the bad men to get his fire. When he got there, however, he found that they had two men who guarded the fire day and night. They were big men and had big spears, and bows and arrows too. So the poor man could not get his fire away from them. He begged them to let him have just a little of it to carry back to his wife and children, but they only laughed at him.

So for several days the good Eskimos had a terrible time. It was very cold and they could not make a fire with anything. At last, one night, the father Eskimo thought of a plan. He called for the little owl, Kerayule, who makes no noise when he flies.

"Please, little owl, will you help us?" the Eskimo man asked him. "You see we have no fire, and we are cold. Please, will you get our fire back for us from the bad men who took it away?"

"How can I do that?" asked the little owl. "I would like to help you, but they have spears and bows and arrows. Besides, they are much stronger than I am. How do you think I could get the fire?"

"You make no noise when you fly," the Eskimo man replied. "They will not hear you coming in the night. Also you can see in the darkness, and you can go straight to their igloo. The window in the top of it will be open, and you can look in and see how you can get the fire for us."

"I never thought of that," said the little owl. "I think maybe I can get the fire for you. I can see in the darkness and I make no noise at all when I fly."

So the little owl set off through the dark night to the igloo where the bad men lived.

99

Carefully the owl flew over the igloo and he did not make a sound. He looked into the window at the top where the smoke came out. He saw the fire—just one small stick burning in the fire pit. Also he saw one of the bad men sitting by it. He seemed to be asleep. The little owl hovered lower and alighted without a sound on the edge of the window. Silently, like a great soft feather, the little owl fluttered down into the igloo.

Right by the fire pit, the little owl landed on the floor and the man did not see him. Maybe he was asleep, but the little owl was not sure. Hopping softly across to the stick of fire, the little owl took the unburned end in his mouth, and with a great flutter, flew straight up through the open window in the top of the igloo. As he did, the man awakened. He grabbed his bow and arrow to shoot the little owl, but was too late. Out into the night sailed the little owl, through the darkness. He flew straight to the igloo of the Eskimos.

The children were watching for the little owl, and soon they saw the fire come flying through the black sky.

"Look!" shouted the little girl. "See the sparkling fire coming!"

And to this day the Eskimos at Hooper Bay call the little owl "sparkling fire owl," or Kennreirk in their language. Sometimes in the springtime, when the sparkling fire owl comes to Hooper Bay and hovers around the people, they will listen closely to see if they can hear him make any noise. Sometimes—very rarely—he makes a little snapping with his beak, or a flutter with his wings. If the people can hear him make any noise they are very glad, for that is the best of good omens. They say the little sparkling fire owl is sending them good luck. If they go hunting they are sure to get a seal, or an eider duck, or a fat fish.

Dominik-Tekun

A BASQUE LEGEND

By Frances Carpenter

"Kerchoo-oo-oo-oo!"

Manesh sneezes so loudly that he wakes Gatua, the cat, who is sleeping in front of the fireplace. His grandmother looks up from her spinning and cries out quickly "Dominik-tekun, which is, as everyone knows, just one other way of saying, "God bless you."

"Why do you always cry 'Dominik-tekun' whenever we sneeze, Amatchi?" Mayi asks her grandmother.

"So that the bad fairies may not carry you off as they did the poor babes of the House of Garibay," is the old woman's reply. "You see, when we sneeze we put ourselves in the hands of the fairies that fill the air all about us. Now the fairies and witches must all disappear when they hear the name of the good God that takes care of us. We must say 'God bless you' when we sneeze to drive them away."

"Did the fairies carry live babies away from the House of Garibay?" Manesh asks curiously.

"That they did!" says Grandmother. "Whenever a baby was born into that house there was the greatest rejoicing, for the Garibays were good people who dearly loved children. But their joy never lasted, for scarcely had they taken the tiny newcomer into their arms when something always happened and the babe disappeared. One! Two! Three! Four!—Four fine sturdy infants had vanished one after the other from the very arms of their nurse, and the good Garibays did not know what to think.

"At last the time drew near for the birth of their fifth child. The house of Garibay was filled with excitement. The father and mother, the menservants and the maidservants, all put their heads together to try to find a way to keep this baby from disappearing. But as they did not know what it was that caused their infants to vanish, they could think of no sure means of preventing it from happening again.

"The baby was born—such a beautiful child that it looked like an angel. As those of the House of Garibay stood by its cradle they all fell to weeping, for the thought of losing so lovely a child was more than they could bear without tears.

"At the same time, out on the highroad there came walking, softly, softly, a certain young man who was really a thief. He had heard of the birth of the fifth child of the Garibays, and he said to himself: 'They will be so delighted and there will be such confusion that they will pay no attention to me. It is a fine time for me

to steal a fat sheep out of their flock.' And he made his way on tip-toe through the bushes near the house, where to his surprise he met an old woman.

" 'What are you doing here, my son?' she said.

" 'I am going to steal a fat sheep out of the flock of the House of Garibay,' he answered. 'There has just been born to that house a beautiful child. They will surely take no notice of my doings in the midst of their excitement.'

" 'I too am going to the House of Garibay,' the old woman cried with a chuckle. 'I am the fairy who has carried off all their infants and now I am going to get the one that is just born.'

" 'And how can you do that?' the young thief asked her.

" 'Easily, easily!' the fairy woman boasted, 'when a child sneezes in that house no one ever thinks to say Dominik-tekun. It will be the same with the new-born one. It will sneeze and I shall be able to grab it from the nurse and fly away with it through the chimney.'

"After that the young man and the old woman parted; and both went on their different ways to the House of Garibay. The young thief stopped for a moment to peer into the window of the kitchen, where to his surprise he saw that all of the household, gathered about the child's cradle, had great tears streaming down over their cheeks.

"Now although this young man was truly a thief, he had a soft heart. He felt very sorry for these poor weeping people. Hardly thinking what he was doing, he knocked on their door. The Master opened it to him and invited him into the kitchen.

" 'Why all this weeping, good people?' he cried. 'I had thought that today there would be only rejoicing in the House of Garibay.'

" 'Ah, we do indeed rejoice greatly,' the Master explained, 'but we fear the disaster that is sure to come on us. Our child has been born, but ah, but—' And he fell to weeping again.

" 'But what, O Master of the House of Garibay?' asked the soft-hearted thief.

" 'It is that our children are all spirited away from us almost as soon as they take their first breath. We have already lost four, one after the other, and now we weep as we wait for the turn of this poor little one.'

" 'Is that all?' cried the soft-hearted thief. 'I will help you. Yes, I will help you, even if I should have to lose my fat sheep. A few moments ago I was out on the highroad, walking ever so softly

toward your house, for I had it in mind to steal a fat sheep out of your flock. As I came through the bushes I met an old woman who boasted to me that she was the fairy that steals your babies away, and from her I learned the charm that will save that little one lying there in his cradle. Let the nurse take the child up into her arms, and be sure that she does just as I tell her.'

"Wondering, the nurse clasped the babe to her breast. Feeling the cool air upon its head, the child sneezed, 'Kerchoo-oo,' and at once the soft-hearted thief called out loudly, 'Dominik-tekun' or 'God bless you!' A shrill scream filled the kitchen, while from behind the door a voice screeched:

" 'You have betrayed me. Curses on you, young man! A thousand curses be upon your wicked head!' And with a rush the old fairy woman flew across the room to the fireplace and went up through the chimney.

"The baby was saved! The Master of the House of Garibay fell down on his knees, weeping with joy and crying out his thanks to the soft-hearted thief for saving his child. Then he led him out to his flock of sheep and bade him choose the fattest of all as his reward.

"Since then, thanks to this young man, not a child has disappeared from all the country about the House of Garibay; for with each sickness or sneeze, the mothers hasten to cry, just as I do, 'Dominik-tekun,' or 'God bless you,' and the wicked fairies are forced to fly straight away."

The Fox and the Crane

The Fox, according to most of the old stories, is a very sly and cunning animal, always ready to play a trick on someone.

One day a Fox invited a Crane to dinner, promising her an unusually fine feast. When the Crane arrived the table was set with two large flat soup plates, filled with steaming soup which smelled very good indeed. The Fox eagerly lapped up his portion and helped himself to another plateful, saying all the time that he had the most wonderful cook in the world, and that it gave him the greatest pleasure to invite his friends to join him whenever he had any particular choice food to offer.

All this time the poor Crane, who had not bothered to eat any lunch because she was looking forward to enjoying a fine dinner at the Fox's house, was unable to get even the tiniest sip of the soup. Her bill was so long and the soup plate so shallow that, twist and turn as she would, she could wet only the very tip of her tongue, and got no food at all.

The Fox never seemed to notice that, but of course he was laughing to himself all the time, which was very rude of him.

Before the Crane left she invited the Fox to dine with her one week from that day.

"Well, Mr. Fox," said the Crane to herself, as she was going home, hungrier than ever, "two can play at this game."

So the Crane prepared her feast in jars with long narrow necks. She could thrust her bill deep down, and pick up delicious bits of fish and fat, juicy bugs, while the Fox, unable to get his big nose anywhere near the food, had to look on all through the dinner, getting hungrier every minute.

You see, it never pays to be smart at the expense of another person.

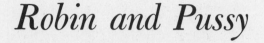

Robin and Pussy

Little Robin Redbreast sat upon a tree,
Up went Pussy Cat, and down went he;
Down came Pussy Cat, and away Robin ran;
Says little Robin Readbreast, "Catch me if you can!"

Little Robin Redbreast jumped upon a wall,
Pussy Cat jumped after him, and almost got a fall.
Little Robin chirped and sang, and what did Pussy say?
Pussy Cat said "Mew, mew," and Robin flew away.

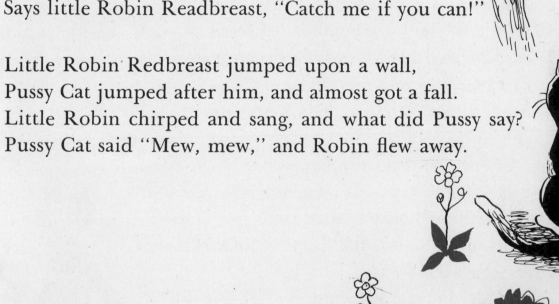

The Silly Old Woman

There was an old woman, as I've heard tell,
She went to market her eggs to sell;
She went to market all on a market day,
And she fell asleep on the king's highway.

There came by a peddler whose name was Stout.
He cut her petticoats all round about;
He cut her petticoats up to her knees,
Which made the old woman to shiver and freeze.

When this old woman first did wake,
She began to shiver and she began to shake;
She began to wonder, and she began to cry,
"Oh, deary, deary me, this is none of I!"

"But if it be I, as I do hope it be,
I've a little dog at home, and he'll know me;
If it be I, he'll wag his little tail,
And if it be not I, he'll loudly bark and wail."

Home went the old woman, all in the dark;
Up got the little dog and he began to bark;
He began to bark, so she began to cry,
"Oh, deary, deary me, this is none of I!"

Old Rhyme

The Special Fourth of July

By Lavinia R. Davis

The Fourth of July dawned cool and clear. The clock in the village church struck seven. Down in the green river valley below the village the Farrells' big white farmhouse was very quiet. None of the four Farrell children were up in the barn. Nobody was on the swing under the apple tree. And nobody except Buff the cocker spaniel was in the big garden. All of the four Farrells were fast asleep. Suddenly in the distance there was a loud bang!

Johnny Farrell, nine, and the oldest of the family woke up and put on his glasses. Bang. Bang. BANG! There were more loud noises coming from the direction of the main road.

Suddenly Johnny Farrell understood. It was the Fourth of July and somebody was setting off firecrackers! Johnny jerked on his

striped jersey and his khaki shorts and rushed into Dickie's room. Dickie Farrell was seven and he was still fast asleep.

Johnny shook him and pulled off his blankets. "Wake up!" he said. "It's the Fourth of July!"

Dickie always woke up slowly. His brown hair was touseled and his eyes were half shut. He looked like a very sleepy mouse and he sounded cross. "Wh-what is it?" he said. "L-l-leave me alone!"

Johnny shrugged his shoulders and moved on to Cynthia's room. Dickie was always cross before breakfast. He might have known.

Cynthia, who was almost six, was up and trying to do her own hair. "It's the Fourth of July," Johnny said.

Cynthia nodded to him in the mirror. "I know it," she said. "The day Mummy and Daddy take us on a picnic."

Every year the Farrell family had a Fourth of July picnic. That

114

is every year except this one. Mummy and Daddy wouldn't be home for the Fourth of July and there wouldn't be any picnic.

Johnny went on down the hall and into Mary Jane's room. Mary Jane was only two. Right now she reached for her rubber duck, while Bridget, the nurse, tried to comb her tight yellow curls. "Hold still, pet," Bridget said and pulled on the comb.

Mary Jane didn't hold still and the comb pulled hard. "Ouch," said Mary Jane. "OH! Oh! Ouch!"

"It's the Fourth of July," Johnny said. This time Bridget pulled on another curl just as Mary Jane made a rush toward Johnny.

"Ouch," said Mary Jane again. "OH! OUCH!"

Johnny shook his head and went downstairs for breakfast. With Mother and Father away nobody seemed to realize that the Fourth of July was supposed to be special at all.

In a little while Dickie and Cynthia came down and had their breakfast. Then Cynthia went upstairs for her doll and Dickie went up to the barn to feed Tinky, his little two-months-old goat.

The Farrells' cows lived up in the barn; and so did Tinky whom Dickie had bought with his very own money; and so did the five Muscovy ducks that belonged to Johnny. Seth, the Farrells' farmer, took care of the cows. The boys took care of the goat and the ducks; and Cynthia who owned Buff the cocker took care of him. Buttercup, the small brown and white cat, who liked to sleep in Tinky's stall really belonged to Mary Jane, but she was too little to take care of her so Dickie did it for her.

Right now, as Johnny Farrell came up the hill, Dickie was giving Tinky her bottle while Buttercup wove in and out between his legs waiting for her milk. Johnny gave his ducks water and scattered their grain. For once it didn't seem much fun to watch them squawk and scuttle for the biggest bits. "Let's celebrate the Fourth of July," Johnny said, now that Dickie was really awake. "Let's do something special!"

"How about a p-pet p-parade?" Dickie said stammering the way he did when he was excited.

Johnny shook his head gloomily. "Wouldn't be any fun with Mummy and Daddy away."

"We might g-get them r-ready just in case," Dickie said. "Just in case Daddy got home."

Johnny didn't feel like doing anything just in case. He left Dickie brushing Tinky and drifted down to the house to see what the rest of the family were doing. Mary Jane was in her pen playing with her blocks. Cynnie washed out her doll clothes at the garden hose while Buff hid under the privet hedge in case she thought of

washing him. Johnny looked at the two girls and sighed. The little kids were doing the things they did every day.

Bang. Bang. BANG. Johnny heard more firecrackers down on the main road. For the first time Johnny had an idea for something special. He was going to get some firecrackers himself!

Mother and Daddy didn't think much of firecrackers. In fact they didn't like firecrackers at all. But this year they weren't around to have the picnic, so surely they wouldn't mind if Johnny went off on his own bicycle to buy some firecrackers with his own money.

Johnny dashed upstairs and got the forty-six cents he had saved to buy war stamps. He put the money in his pocket and hurried out to his bicycle. Just then the telephone rang. It rang one short ring and two long rings. One short ring and two long rings! Johnny listened. He knew it was his family's ring, and he wondered why Mary, the cook, didn't answer. The ring came again.

"Hello," said Johnny. "Hello?"

"Hello?" said Central. "Berkeley 981 ring 1-2? Long distance calling Mr. Jonathan Farrell, Jr."

"It's me," said Johnny and now he was so excited he forgot the proper way to talk on a telephone. "It's Johnny."

"Go ahead, New York," Central said, and then the next instant Johnny heard Daddy's voice over the telephone.

"Johnny?" said Daddy. "Johnny, boy, is that you?"

"Yes," said Johnny. "Y-yes," and now he almost stuttered like Dickie. "How are you, Dad?"

"Fine," said Dad. "And I've got a big piece of news. You've got a new little brother. His name's Robert and he was born early this morning on the Fourth of July."

"Golly!" said Johnny. And then again, "Golly!"

"Mother's fine," Daddy said. "And she sent you her love. Will you tell the others?"

"Yes!" said Johnny. "You bet!" and he slammed down the receiver.

"Ive-got-a-new-brother-his-name's-Robert!" Johnny shouted. "And his birthday is the Fourth of July." He dashed across the lawn. Then he saw Mary, the cook, coming down from the garden with the luncheon carrots. Bridget, Mary Jane, Cynnie and Buff were starting for a walk.

"We've got a new brother," Johnny shouted again. "His name's Robert and his birthday is the Fourth of July."

"What?"

"When?"

"Well glory be!"

Everybody talked at once, and nobody noticed when Dickie came down the hill leading Tinky. "What's happened?" he said. "What's g-g-going on?"

"Brother!" Johnny and Cynthia raced to tell him. "Robert. A baby brother born this morning."

"N-no!" said Dickie. "No-no!"

They had just convinced him that it was really true when the telephone rang again. Johnny answered it, and this time it was Grandma Waring who lived just the other side of Berkeley.

"Isn't it wonderful?" she said and her voice sounded as excited as Johnny felt. "Isn't it marvelous? You've all got to come over for lunch, even Mary Jane, so we can celebrate. I'll come down in the car in half an hour to get you."

"Good!" said Johnny. "Swell!" Then he hung up and told the others.

"We're going to Grandma's!" said Cynthia and twirled around the lawn. "Oh, boy. I want to take Buff."

"Going to Gwandma's," said Mary Jane and copied Cynthia until she fell down. "Mawy Jane's going to Gwandma's and so'th Buttercup."

"G-good!" said Dickie. "G-good!"

Johnny didn't say anything at all. He just rushed upstairs and put the money back into his bank until he had enough money for three war stamps. He hadn't bought the firecrackers and he was glad. This Fourth of July was special enough without them!

The Hare and the Tortoise

A Hare was very much surprised one day when a Tortoise suggested that they run a race.

"Why, by all means let's race," said the Hare, "but of course you know that you will be left far behind. Everyone knows how fast I run, but as for you—you cannot run at all. You carry that clumsy shell everywhere on your back, and besides those funny little legs of yours were not made for running. Why don't you ask the Snail to race with you?"

"I prefer to race with you," said the Tortoise. "Let us get the Fox to mark the course, and stand by to see that the race is run fairly."

"Very well," said the Hare.

They agreed to race to a certain tree some distance down the road, and as soon as the Fox barked the signal the race began.

The Tortoise started off at his usual slow pace, and the Hare,

hopping briskly, soon left him yards behind. Then as it was a warm day, Mr. Hare decided to take a nap. When he waked he noticed that the sun, which had shone high above them when the race started, was now almost ready to set. He yawned and streched himself, and wondered how far the old Tortoise had crawled in all this time. "Well," he said, with another big yawn, "I'll just run over to the big tree and have a chat with the Fox while we are waiting for the Tortoise."

In about a minute the Hare had almost reached the tree. What was that strange dark object at its foot? Had somebody placed a rock there since the morning? How odd! No! It wasn't a rock at all; it was the slow old Tortoise, already at the end of the race course, and resting quietly in his shell! And there, by his side, was the Fox, sitting on his haunches with a broad grin on his face.

It was a long time before the other animals stopped teasing the Hare about his famous race with the Tortoise. They never let the Hare forget that even the swiftest runner must always be on his toes if he hopes to win a race.

The Frog Who Wanted to be as Big as the Ox

An Ox, grazing in the meadow, stepped on a young Frog and killed him. The Frog's brothers, who saw the accident, hopped home in a hurry. They told their mother that an enormous animal had crushed their brother.

"How big was this animal?" asked the old Frog.

"The biggest animal in the world," answered the little Frogs.

"Nonsense!" said the old Frog, "Was he as big as this?" and she puffed herself up to twice her usual size.

"Bigger, oh, much bigger!" cried all the little Frogs at once.

The old Frog took another deep breath, and puffed herself up even more. She was a vain old thing, and foolishly thought that by puffing she could make herself as big as any animal on earth. "Was he this big?" she croaked.

"Stop, mother, you will only hurt yourself. You are nowhere near as big as that huge beast we saw!"

But the old Frog wouldn't stop—not she. She puffed and she puffed, and she puffed, and she PUFFED until she POPPED! Little pieces of her flew in all directions. And that was the end of her!

Little Orphant Annie

James Whitcomb Riley

Little Orphant Annie's come to our house to stay,
An' wash the cups an' saucers up, an' brush the crumbs away,
An' shoo the chickens off the porch, an' dust the hearth, an' sweep,
An' make the fire, an' bake the bread, an' earn her board an' keep;
An' all us other children, when the supper things is done,
We set around the kitchen fire an' has the mostest fun
A-lis'nin' to the witch-tales 'at Annie tells about,
An' the Gobble-uns 'at gits you

        Ef you

           Don't

              Watch

                Out!

Onc't there was a little boy wouldn't say his prayers,—
So when he went to bed at night, away up stairs,
His Mammy heerd him holler, an' his Daddy heerd him bawl,
An' when they turn't the kivvers down, he wasn't there at all!
An' they seeked him in the rafter-room, an' cubby-hole, an' press,
An' they seeked him up the chimbly-flue, an' ever'wheres, I guess;
But all they ever found was thist his pants and roundabout:—

An' the Gobble-uns'll git you
        Ef you
            Don't
                Watch
                    Out!

An' one time a little girl 'ud allus laugh an' grin,
An' make fun of ever'one, an' all her blood and kin;
An' onc't, when there was "company," an' ole folks was there,
She mocked 'em an' shocked 'em, an' said she didn't care!
An' thist as she kicked her heels, an' turn't to run an' hide,
They was two great big Black Things a-standin' by her side,
An' they snatched her through the ceilin' 'fore she knowed
                      what she's about!

An' the Gobble-uns'll git you
        Ef you
            Don't
                Watch
                    Out!

An' little Orphant Annie says, when the blaze is blue,
An' the lamp-wick sputters, an' the wind goes woo-oo!
An' you hear the crickets quit, an' the moon is gray,
An' the lightnin'-bugs in dew is all squenched away,—
You better mind yer parents, an' yer teachers fond and dear,
An' churish them 'at loves you, an' dry the orphant's tear,
An' he'p the pore an' needy ones 'at clusters all about,
Er the Gobble-uns'll git you
        Ef you
            Don't
                Watch
                    Out!

Doll in the Grass

A NORWEGIAN FOLK TALE

By Ingri and Edgar Parin d'Aulaire

Once on a time there was a king who had twelve sons. When they had grown big he told them they must go out into the world and win themselves a wife each, but these wives must be able to spin and weave and sew a shirt in one day, else he wouldn't have them for daughters-in-law.

To each he gave a horse and a new suit of mail, and they rode out into the world to look for wives; but when they had travelled a bit of the way, they said they wouldn't have Cinderlad, their youngest brother, with them—he was good for nothing, they said.

Well, Cinderlad had to stay behind, there was no help for that, and he didn't know what to do or whither to turn. He grew so downcast he got off his horse and sat down in the tall grass to weep. But when he had sat a little while, one of the tufts in the grass began to stir and move, and out of it came a tiny white thing. And when it came nearer, Cinderlad saw it was a lovely little maiden, only she was so very small and tiny. She went up to him and asked if he would come down below and see the "Doll in the Grass."

Yes, he'd be very happy, and so he went.

Now when he got down, there sat the Doll in the Grass on a chair. She was so lovely and so beautifully dressed, and she asked Cinderlad whither he was going, and what was his business.

So he told her how there were twelve brothers of them, and how the king had given them horses and mail, and said they must each go out into the world and find them a wife who could spin and weave and sew a shirt in a day.

"But if you'll be my wife, I'll not go a step further," said Cinderlad to the Doll in the Grass.

Yes, she was willing enough, and spun and wove and sewed the shirt, but it was so tiny, so very, very tiny, not longer than—so long.

So Cinderlad set off home with it; but when he brought it out, he was almost ashamed, it was so small. Still the king said he should have her, and so Cinderlad set off, glad and happy to fetch his little sweetheart. When he got to the Doll in the Grass he wished to take her up before him on his horse, but she wouldn't have that; for she said she would sit and drive along in a silver spoon, and that she had two small white horses to draw her. So off they set, he on his horse and she on her silver spoon, and the horses that drew her were two small, white mice. Cinderlad always kept the other side of the road, he was so afraid lest he should ride over her, who was so very small and tiny. When they had gone a bit of the way, they came to a great lake. Here Cinderlad's horse got frightened and shied across the road and upset the spoon, and the Doll in the Grass fell into the water. Cinderlad became very sad, because he didn't know how he could ever get her out again; but in a little while up came a merman with her, and now she had grown to the size of other human beings, and far lovelier than she had been before. So he took her up before him on his horse and rode home.

When Cinderlad got home, all his brothers had come back, each with his sweetheart. But these were all so ugly and foul and wicked, and they had done nothing but fight and pull their sweethearts' hair on the way home. And on their heads they had a kind of hat that was daubed over with tar and soot, and so the rain had run down off the hats onto their faces till they got far uglier and nastier than they had been before. When his brothers saw Cinderlad and his sweetheart, they were all as jealous as jealous could be of her; but the king was so overjoyed with them both that he drove all the others away, and so Cinderlad held his wedding feast with the Doll in the Grass. And after that they lived well and happily together a long, long time, and if they're not dead, why, they're alive still.

Nursery Rhymes From China

Isaac Taylor Headland, *Translator*

THE COW
"There's a cow on the mountain,"
　　The old saying goes,
On her legs are four feet,
　　On her feet are eight toes;
Her tail is behind
　　On the end of her back;
And her head is in the front
　　On the end of her neck!

THE MOUSE
He climbed up the candlestick,
　　The little mousy brown,
To steal and eat tallow,
　　And he couldn't get down.
He called for his grandma,
　　But his grandma was in town,
So he doubled up into a wheel
　　And rolled himself down!

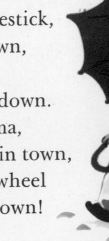

The Bald Old Woman

On the top of the mount,
    By the road, on a stone—
Or a big pile of bricks—
    Sat a bald-headed crone.

On her head were three hairs,
    Which you'll reckon were thin,
In which she was trying
    To wear a jade pin.

She put it in once,
    But once it fell out;
She put it in twice,
    But twice it fell out.

But the old woman said,
    "I know what I'm about,
I'll not put it in,
    And it cannot fall out."

Miss T

By Walter de la Mare

It's a very odd thing—
　　As odd as can be—
That whatever Miss T. eats
　　Turns into Miss T.
Porridge and apples,
　　Mince, muffins and mutton,
Jam, junket, jumbles—
　　Not a rap, not a button
It matters; the moment
　　They're out of her plate,
Though shared by Miss Butcher
　　And sour Mr. Bate,
Tiny and cheerful,
　　And neat as can be,
Whatever Miss T. eats
　　Turns into Miss T.

Nonsense Verses

By Laura E. Richards

Nicholas Ned,
He lost his head,
And put a turnip on instead;
But then, ah, me!
He could not see,
So he thought it was night, and he went to bed.

Ponsonby Perks,
He fought the Turks,
Performing many wonderful works;
He killed over forty.
High-minded and haughty,
And cut off their heads with smiles and smirks.

Harriet Hutch,
Her conduct was such,
Her uncle remarked it would conquer the Dutch;
She boiled her new bonnet,
And breakfasted on it,
And rode to the moon on her grandmother's crutch.

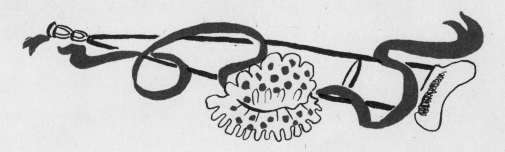

The Shire Colt

By Zhenya and Jan Gay

Penny Farm is in the Cotswold Hills in England. There is a big stone house, and a little stone church, and three stone barns. There are acres and acres of green fields that roll over the hills and down into the valleys. There are orchards and meadows, berry brambles, a lily pond, a brook.

No one knew Penny Farm better than Djuna, the big Shire mare. All through the year she worked for Farmer Penny. In the Spring she plowed the fields. In the summer she carted the hay. In the autumn she brought in the fruit from the orchards. In the winter she drew the wagon of heavy cordwood down from the hills.

136

Djuna had a long flowing mane, a long tail, and clusters of curls around her feet. She was strong and beautiful as she went down the road with her mane flying in the breeze, and her great hooves pounding Clip-Clop, Clip-Clop.

Last spring another horse plowed the fields of Penny Farm. Djuna was busy with something else. She had a new foal. He was a weak little fellow, so she had to take a great deal of care of him. The colt had a brown coat and brown eyes, a curly brown mane and a curly brown tail. When Farmer Penny saw the colt he said, "There is nothing else to do but to call this colt Brownie."

Brownie had little pointed ears, and a soft inquisitive nose. At first he wasn't strong. When he tried to stand up his legs wobbled. When he tried to walk he fell down. For quite a long time he lived in the stable, in a big box stall with a bed of yellow straw. When he was tired he lay down in the straw. Djuna lay beside him to keep him warm.

One day in April when the sun shone brightly, Farmer Penny led Brownie and Djuna out of the stable into the farmyard. Brownie was frightened, and stayed close to his mother. He saw a great many things that were new to him. He saw the outside of the stone stable where he lived. He saw tall stacks of cordwood. He saw a big pig and her little pigs. He saw a rooster and hen and little chickens. He saw ducks that waddled when they walked.

After Brownie had spent several days in the farmyard, he knew the chickens and ducks and pigs. He knew another horse and a cow. He was afraid of the cow's horns. He knew which door of the stable led to his stall. Then he discovered the gate. Beyond the gate there was a great green world, stretching as far as he could see. There were

hills and valleys with hedgerows between the fields. He didn't know what all these things were, but he was eager to find out.

Now Brownie was strong enough to go out and live in the fields. Farmer Penny put a halter on Djuna and led her out of the farmyard. Brownie followed at her side. He could walk now without falling down. He could even run a little way if he didn't try to go too fast. They went past the pond where the ducks were swimming, past the orchard where the apples trees were in bloom. They went through a gate, across a field, through another gate. Then Farmer Penny left them.

The summer was so fine that they stayed out of doors all day and night. They made their home under a special chestnut tree. Farmer Penny put a water trough there, so Djuna and Brownie could have a drink of water when they wanted one. During those first days in the field everything that Brownie saw surprised him. He would prick up his ears and kick up his heels to see what would happen next.

When it grew dark Brownie wondered why they didn't return to the stable. That was what he had done when he stayed in the

farmyard. Now that they had moved to the field, he found that they were going to sleep under the chestnut tree. Djuna lay down on the ground. Brownie lay beside her. He saw the stars twinkling far away in the sky. He saw the yellow lights in Farmer Penny's house. He felt his mother warm and comforting beside him. Then he went to sleep.

The next morning, and all of the first days in the field, he kept close beside Djuna. She was happy to be in the meadow, and wandered from place to place, munching the tender grass. When Brownie saw her eating grass, he thought it must be good, so he tried to nibble it, too. But his teeth weren't big enough yet, and he had to wait until he was a little older to find out how good the grass tasted.

Brownie was growing stronger every day. After a run in the field he would come back and lie down under the tree. One day he discovered the flowers growing in the grass. "This is a wonderful world," he said to himself, "the grass is soft, the flowers smell sweet, and all I have to do this summer is to lie here and kick my heels."

Now Brownie grew bolder. He didn't stay beside Djuna all the time, but went off by himself through the field to see what he could find. One day he discovered that other animals lived in his field. The first one he found was a queer spotted fellow that sat in the grass and looked at him with big bulging eyes. As usual when Brownie was surprised, he pricked up his ears and was ready to run to his mother when the frog hopped away through the grass.

Just then Djuna came up to him, and Brownie peeped fearfully around her to see whether the frog had come back. Djuna said to him, "You mustn't be afraid of the other animals. They won't hurt

you. Make friends of them and play with them. One day soon I expect you will meet a rabbit. There are many rabbits in this field."

A few days later Brownie was taking a nap in the sun. A noise waked him and he turned to see what it was. There beside him was the strangest animal he had ever seen. It had two long flopping ears, bigger than his own. For a few minutes they stared at each other. Then Brownie went back to sleep. He was soon wakened again. This time he saw half a dozen rabbits. The first one had called in all his brothers to see this strange long-legged colt sleeping in the grass.

Then Brownie remembered that his mother had told him to make friends with the other animals and play with them. He stood up and was just going to invite them to play when all the rabbits hopped quickly away. Brownie was so much bigger than they were that the rabbits thought he might step on them. The colt was disappointed. He tried to find the rabbits, but they had all disappeared into their burrows.

Brownie decided that if no one would play with him he would play by himself. There was a new game he had invented several days ago, the game of Rolling on Your Back. He lay down on the grass and pawed the air with his four feet. M-m-m, how good that felt, he thought, as he rolled over and over on the grassy knoll.

One day as he walked along beside his mother, Brownie sniffed at the hedgerow. He had admired the May blossoms and the glossy holly leaves for a long time. Djuna was busy eating grass, walking along with her head close to the ground. Brownie stuck his nose into the thorn tree. With a whinny of pain he ran to his mother. He had a thorn in his nose. Oh-oh, how it hurt! Finally the thorn fell out. Djuna took him to the water trough to cool his poor nose in the water. "You must be careful," she said, "about poking your nose into unknown places."

Farmer Penny took Djuna and Brownie to a new field. A lovely field. A brook ran along one side of it. Brownie went for a walk through the long grass that grew beside the brook. All at once he saw something very strange at his feet. It looked like a little umbrella. Not one umbrella but dozens. All this corner of the field was sprinkled with mushrooms.

Brownie found the mushrooms most exciting. He put his hoof on one and it disappeared. He wanted to eat one. Quickly he snapped it off with his lips. He was afraid to eat in in front of the others, for fear they would chase him. He galloped off to another corner of the field with the mushroom in his mouth. When he got there he had lost it, but he had had great fun taking it, just the same.

Another day when he was out exploring, he went back to the

brook. He slid down the steep bank. To his surprise he found water in the brook. He slipped and got quite wet. He switched his tail and shook his head to get the water out of his ears. While he was there he took a long drink. Then he climbed up the bank and scampered off to tell his mother his latest discovery—that the brook was full of water like the trough.

While he was running away from the brook, he heard something buzzing, and felt a bumping on his back. He tried to shake it off, but it wouldn't go. He ran and jumped, and tried to switch his tail, but his tail wouldn't reach the fly. The only thing to do was to go to Djuna who had such a splendid long tail that with just one flick she got rid of the fly for him.

One day Brownie found himself quite alone in a far corner of the field. The wind blew, and ruffled up his ears. Little drops hit him, pat-pat, drop-drop, on his head and his back and in his face. The rain came on harder. He was frightened, and hugged up close against a tree trunk. The wind howled. The rain came down in sheets. He was very frightened.

Finally he heard Djuna neighing. She came galloping across the field to him. She stood beside him, and nuzzled him, and told him that everything was all right. How warm she was! How big and strong! He never felt afraid when she was beside him. She stayed with him until the storm was over. Then she went on eating grass.

After the rain everything smelled so good. He stood on a little knoll and sniffed the rain-washed air. Then he went on a journey of exploration. The gate to the next meadow had been left open. He crossed a bridge over the brook. He had never walked on any-

thing but grass before. His hooves made a hollow sound on the planks of the bridge.

Brownie had been curious about some little white specks that moved about in this field. Now that he was close to them, he saw that they had four legs. They ran and jumped. He ran after these lambs to play with them. But like the rabbits, the lambs ran away from him. They didn't disappear into holes in the ground, they just played by themselves. Brownie was sorry they wouldn't play with him, they looked so white and fluffy.

In another corner of the field he saw some of those strange beasts that he just barely remembered seeing in the farmyard a long time ago. The big ones wore long horns and were not nearly as nice as his mother. The little ones were about his own size, but they couldn't run as fast. He chased them, and they ran bawling away to their mothers.

Brownie walked over toward the next field. Beyond the fence he saw what he had been waiting for a long time, a play-fellow who looked like himself. Another colt stood in the next meadow. The trouble was that the gate wasn't open, so the two little colts stood on either side of it, whinnying to each other and wishing that they could play together.

Farmer Penny was crossing the fields going home to his tea. He opened the gate and let the colts into the same field. They started to play together. They gamboled and raced, kicking their heels high into the air. Brownie said to the other colt, "I don't care if the rabbits and the lambs and the calves won't play with me. You are the best playmate of all."

Then Farmer Penny took Brownie back to his own field by the

brook. Djuna was waiting there for him. Brownie told her all his adventures. "You are growing up," she said to him. "It is a good thing, too, because soon I am going to leave you in the daytime and go back to work in the fields. This is the haying season. I am going to draw the cart to carry the hay to the barns so we will have something to eat next winter."

Brownie was really very sorry to see his mother go away, although he now had the other colt to play with. But when he saw her pulling the cart, he was proud of her because she was so beautiful and strong. He ran back to the field to play with the other colt.

Next year, perhaps, when Brownie grows big and strong like Djuna, he too can help with the haying.

Thanksgiving Day

By L. Maria Child

Over the river and through the wood,
    To grandfather's house we go;
        The horse knows the way
        To carry the sleigh
    Through the white and drifted snow

Over the river and through the wood—
    Oh, how the wind does blow!
        It stings the toes,
        And bites the nose,
    As over the ground we go.

Over the river and through the wood
    To have a first-rate play.
        Hear the bells ring,
        "Ting-a-ling-ding!"
    Hurrah for Thanksgiving Day!

Over the river and through the wood,
    Trot fast, my dapple-gray!
       Spring over the ground
       Like a hunting hound!
    For this is Thanksgiving Day.

Over the river and through the wood,
    And straight through the barn-yard gate.
       We seem to go
       Extremely slow—
    It is so hard to wait!

Over the river and through the wood—
    Now grandmother's cap I spy!
       Hurrah for the fun!
       Is the pudding done?
    Hurrah for the pumpkin-pie!

The House That Jack Built

This is the house that Jack built.
This is the Malt,
That lay in the House that Jack built.
This is the Rat,
That ate the Malt,
That lay in the House that Jack built.

This is the Cat
That killed the Rat,
That ate the Malt,
That lay in the House that Jack built.

This is the Dog
That worried the Cat,
That killed the Rat,
That ate the Malt,
That lay in the House that Jack built.

This is the Cow with the crumpled horn,
That tossed the Dog,
That worried the Cat,
That killed the Rat,
That ate the Malt,
That lay in the House that Jack built.

150

This is the Maiden all forlorn,
That milked the Cow with the crumpled horn,
That tossed the Dog,
That worried the Cat,
That killed the Rat,
That ate the Malt,
That lay in the House that Jack built.

This is the Man all tattered and torn,
That kissed the Maiden all forlorn,
That milked the Cow with the crumpled horn,
That tossed the Dog,
That worried the Cat,
That killed the Rat,
That ate the Malt,
That lay in the House that Jack built.

This is the priest all shaven and shorn,
That married the Man all tattered and torn,
That kissed the Maiden all forlorn,
That milked the Cow with the crumpled horn,
That tossed the Dog,
That worried the Cat,
That killed the Rat,
That ate the Malt,
That lay in the House that Jack built.

This is the Cock that crowed in the morn.
That waked the Priest all shaven and shorn,
That married the Man all tattered and torn,
That kissed the Maiden all forlorn,
That milked the Cow with the crumpled horn,
That tossed the Dog,
That worried the Cat,
That killed the Rat,
That ate the Malt,
That lay in the House that Jack built.

This is the Farmer who sowed the corn,
That fed the Cock that crowed in the morn,
That waked the Priest all shaven and shorn,
That married the Man all tattered and torn,
That kissed the Maiden all forlorn,
That milked the Cow with the crumpled horn,
That tossed the Dog,
That worried the Cat,
That killed the Rat,
That ate the Malt,
That lay in the House that Jack built.

The Train That Would Not Stay on the Track

By Caroline D. Emerson

Once upon a time there was a train who was tired of staying on the track.

"Why must I run on a track all the days of my life?" asked the train.

"You had much better stay where you are," said the track. "I was laid for you to run on and you were made to run on me. Everything is better off in this world if it stays where it belongs."

But the train would not listen.

"I am not going to stay here," he said, and he jumped off the track and began to run along the road.

"Keep off!" cried the automobiles. "This road was made for us. Keep off! Keep off!"

"No such thing!" said the train, "there's plenty of room on the road for me."

He ran on down the road. He stopped at the houses for people and trunks and he stopped at the post office for the mail bags. He ran out to the barns for the milk. Everyone was delighted. It was much easier than to carry everything down to the station. But the train took so long that he never got to the end of his trip!

People waited for their trunks and they never came. The letters in the mail bags were so old that no one troubled to read them. The milk was sour and was no good to anyone. People stopped putting their things on to the train and began to send them by automobile instead.

"There now," said the automobiles, "no one is using you any more. You should have stayed on your track as we told you to. The road is no place for you."

But the train refused to go back to his track. One day he saw a horse running across the fields.

"Why should I stay on a road?" asked the train. "That looks like fun."

He left the road and started off across the fields.

"You mustn't come here!" cried the horse. "This is my field. Keep off! Keep off!"

"No such thing," answered the train, "there's plenty of room in this field for me."

Bump, bump, bump went the train across the field until he came to a brook.

"How do I get over this?" asked the train.

"Jump," said the horse.

"I never jumped in my life," said the train, "I always have bridges laid down for me."

"Bridges?" laughed the horse. "You'd better go back where you belong. The track is the place for you."

But the train paid no attention to him for just then he heard an aeroplane up in the air.

"That looks like fun," said the train. "Why should I stay on the ground? I am going to fly."

"Silly," said the horse, "you who can't even jump a brook!"

The train tried to fly. He tried with his front wheels. He tried with his back wheels. He tried with all four wheels. He tried until he was tired.

"Well," said the train, "there appears to be something wrong. I can't fly. People won't ride on me when I bump across the fields and they won't send trunks and mail by me when I run on the road. They say I'm too slow. I don't seem to be good for anything! I might as well stay right here and let my fires go out. No one would miss me!"

The train felt lonely and discouraged. He felt he was no longer of any use in this world. Then an idea flashed through his steam pipes.

"I might go back to my tracks," he thought, "I wonder if they're still there?"

He crept across the field and down the road to the station. There lay the tracks right where he had left them, stretching off in both directions. They looked so safe and smooth! The train gave a great puff of happiness as he climbed back on them.

"It's been lonely without you," said the track. "I was afraid that I would rust away with no one running over me."

At the station there were many people waiting and a pile of trunks and mail bags.

"This is just where I belong," whistled the train, "and everything is better off in this world if he will stay where he belongs though precious few of us know it."

Pippa's Song

By Robert Browning

The year's at the spring
And day's at the morn;
Morning's at seven;
The hill-side's dew-pearled;
The lark's on the wing;
The snail's on the thorn:
God's in his heaven
All's right with the world!

Table Manners

By Gelett Burgess

The Goops they lick their fingers,
  And the Goops lick their knives;
They spill their broth on the table cloth—
  Oh, they lead disgusting lives!

The Goops they talk while eating,
  And loud and fast they chew;
And that is why I'm glad that I
  Am not a Goop—are you?

Limerick

By Edward Lear

There was an Old Person of Ware
Who rode on the back of a bear;
  When they asked, "Does it trot?"
  He said, "Certainly not!
He's a Moppsikon Floppsikon bear!"

Thank You, God

by Ilo Orleans

I thank you, God,
For a hundred things:
For the flower that blooms,
For the bird that sings,
For the sun that shines,
And the rain that drops,
For ice cream,
  and raisins,
   and lollypops.
    Amen.

159

Acknowledgment

The author and the publisher wish to make acknowledgment of their indebtedness to the following publishers:

THE BOBBS-MERRILL COMPANY, for permission to use "Little Orphant Annie" from *Rhymes of Childhood*.

DOUBLEDAY & COMPANY, INC., for permission to use the following stories: "Dominik Tekun" from *Tales of a Basque Grandmother* by Frances Carpenter; "The Ice-Cream Man" from *Taxis and Toadstools* by Rachel Field; *The Shire Colt* by Zhenya and Jan Gay.

DOUBLEDAY & COMPANY, INC., and Methuen & Co. Ltd. (London) for permission to use "The Little Boy Who Wouldn't Get Up," and "The Pirate and the Pickled Onions" from *Forty Good Morning Tales* by Rose Fyleman.

E. P. DUTTON & CO. INC., for permission to use "The Train That Would Not Stay on the Track" from *A Merry-Go-Round of Modern Tales* by Caroline D. Emerson.

HENRY HOLT & COMPANY, INC., for permission to use "Miss T" from *Collected Poems* by Walter de la Mare.

J. B. LIPPINCOTT COMPANY, for permission to use "My Steam Shovel" from *A Steam Shovel for Me* by Vera Edelstadt; and "Table Manners" from *Goops and How to Be Them* by Gelett Burgess.

LITTLE, BROWN & COMPANY, for permission to use "Nonsense Verses" from *Tirra Lirra* by Laura E. Richards, and "Thanksgiving Day" by L. Maria Child.

THE MACMILLAN COMPANY, for permission to use "How the Little Owl's Name Was Changed" from *Beyond the Clapping Mountains* by Charles E. Gillham; and "Valentine to My Mother" from *Poetical Works* by Christina Rossetti.

ILO ORLEANS, for permission to use "I Thank You, God" from *Funday*.

OXFORD UNIVERSITY PRESS, for permission to use "A Strange Little Home" from *All the Year Round* by Alice Gall and Fleming Crew.

THE PLATT & MUNK CO., INC., for permission to use "Mr. Easter Rabbit" by Caroline S. Bailey from *The Children's Hour*.

G. P. PUTNAM'S SONS, for permission to use "Names" from *Hop, Skip, and Jump* by Dorothy Aldis.

FLEMING H. REVELL COMPANY, for permission to use "The Cow," "The Mouse," and "The Bald Old Woman," from *Chinese Mother Goose Rhymes*, translated by Isaac Taylor Headland.

RINEHART & COMPANY, INCORPORATED, for permission to use *The Teacup Whale* by Lydia Gibson.

ROW, PETERSON & COMPANY, for permission to use "The Three Billy Goats Gruff" from *East O' The Sun and West O' The Moon* by Mrs. Gudrun Thorne-Thomsen.

CHARLES SCRIBNER'S SONS, for permission to use "The Rock-a-by-Lady" from *Love Songs of Childhood* by Eugene Field; and "The Special Fourth of July" from *Round Robin* by Lavinia R. Davis.

THE VIKING PRESS, for permission to use "Doll in the Grass," from *East of the Sun and West of the Moon* by Ingri and Edgar Parin d' Aulaire.